Prentice Hall
Writing Skills Test Bank

Linda Whisnant
Guilford Technical Community College

PEARSON

Prentice
Hall

Upper Saddle River, New Jersey 07458

© 2004 by PEARSON EDUCATION, INC.
Upper Saddle River, New Jersey 07458

ISBN 0-13-111628-2

Printed in the United States of America

Contents

PART I

Writing Process Skills

A. Circle the letter of the best choice to answer the following questions or to complete the following sentences.

1. Which one of the following is <u>not</u> a method of early prewriting, the gathering of ideas for a paper?
    a. brainstorming
    b. freewriting
    c. outlining
    d. clustering (also called mapping or branching)

2. In the prewriting stage, a writer should consider which of the following?
    a. what the main point is going to be
    b. grammar
    c. spelling
    d. punctuation

3. After putting onto paper a large number of possible ideas for a paragraph or essay, the writer often needs to _____ before he or she can continue.
    a. reorder them into a formal outline
    b. write the rough draft based on the generated ideas
    c. get rid of ideas that do not pertain to the main point
    d. add more ideas to complete the development

B. Match the method of prewriting with the letter of the description that best fits it.

1. _____ Freewriting

    a. linking ideas visually as they come to you by writing words in circles and drawing lines to connect circles

2. _____ Brainstorming

    b. keeping a regular log of thoughts, feelings, opinions, and observations from which to pull ideas for assignments

3. _____ Clustering

    c. writing a list of words or phrases that come to mind about a topic, without worrying about order

4. _____ Asking questions

    d. writing with an open mind for a specified amount of time, including everything that comes to mind, without thinking about grammar or organization

5. _____ Journaling

    e. exploring a topic by generating your own investigation, as a news reporter would

C. **Here is a list of brainstorming ideas that a student might write for a paragraph on his job at a car wash. Read the list, consider what might be a main idea, and cross out three ideas that the writer will not need to include.**

drying the exterior
dealing with customers
preparing the floors for vacuuming
spraying the dashboard with cleaner
my first car was a green Camaro
cleaning the seats
thanking the customer
aching back from bending over so much
making sure the car is on the rollers correctly
making change for the customer to return with a receipt
spraying and scrubbing the tires
boss really hates it if a person is late
speaking courteously
making sure the windows are rolled up

D. **In the space on the right above, begin a cluster of the items on the left. Use circles and lines to show how the ideas might be grouped or related. Draw at least three circles for words or groups of words.**

E. **In the following list of ideas generated for a paragraph about why your grandfather needs to stop driving, write a K for the details to keep for support and a D for those you would drop because they do not support your point.**

_____ needs glasses, refuses to wear his if they aren't handy
_____ started driving a tractor on the farm when he was twelve
_____ doesn't use turn signals
_____ arthritis in his neck makes it difficult to turn and look over his shoulder
_____ drives an old car that is still in great condition
_____ gets lost easily and will not stop to ask for directions

F. **Make up and write below two more possible support details for the above prewriting list.**

1.

2.

G. **Early in the writing process, a writer must be clear on what his or her purpose is. For each of the following ideas for a paragraph, write next to the topic an E if its purpose is to entertain, I if its purpose is to inform, and a P if it is to persuade.**

1. _____ the steps involved in becoming an American citizen

2. _____ comparing Aunt Irene's snores to a chain saw or jack hammer

3. _____ kinds of grain for bread that are alternatives to traditional wheat

4. _____ to convince the college to add a day to the preregistration period

5. _____ three favorite teachers who influenced Sam's decision to major in education

H.   Imagine you are on a vacation. Write one sample sentence of a postcard back home to each of these two possible audiences. Make sure your sentence matches the intended audience.

1. Write one sentence about your vacation to an elderly uncle. Pretend that this uncle gave you some money for the trip and that he would be interested to know what you are learning.

2. Write one sentence about your vacation to a friend your age who has the same interests as you do.

A. Circle T for true or F for false for each of the following statements about prewriting.

T F 1. Freewriting or brainstorming (or any other method of gathering ideas) occurs only at the beginning of the writing process, and, once finished, is not done again.

T F 2. Exploring a topic is an important step in the prewriting process.

T F 3. After a writer gets ideas on paper by freewriting, brainstorming, or clustering, he or she usually needs to get rid of part of the original material in order to achieve unity.

T F 4. Once a writer discovers a method of prewriting that works well, he or she should always use that same method for any writing task.

T F 5. Keeping a dictionary handy will help a writer spell words correctly during freewriting; correct spelling at this point is important.

B. In the space below, brainstorm at least eight items on one of the following topics. Circle your choice. *(counts as four test items)*

<u>owning a pet</u>   or   <u>maintaining an older car</u>   or   <u>a job you have had</u>

C. In the space below, take the words or phrases from the brainstormed list that you wrote above, and arrange them into clusters to show that you understand the differences between these two methods (brainstorming and clustering). Use each item from the brainstormed list, and draw at least three clusters. *(counts as one test item)*

D. Below are three paragraph topics, each one about the writer's Uncle Jeff. Beside each one, write an abbreviation for what you would predict is the purpose of the writer's paragraph. In the blanks, write E if the purpose is to entertain, I if it is to inform, and <u>P</u> if it is to persuade.

1. _____ Uncle Jeff, or "Sun Man" as he's called, dresses like it's still 1975.

2. _____ Uncle Jeff needs to change jobs soon for the sake of his physical health.

3. _____ Uncle Jeff's experiences with the Peace Corps in Africa motivated him to become a nurse.

E. Here is a list of brainstorming ideas that a student might write for a paragraph on things she enjoyed during a trip to the Florida Keys. Read the list, consider what might

be the main idea, and cross out three ideas that the writer will not need in her paragraph. *(counts as three test items)*

snorkeling around the coral reef
visited a sea turtle hospital
ran out of gas on the longest bridge
lots of unusual shopping opportunities
had a long layover in Atlanta airport
enjoyed eating alligator as an appetizer in Key Largo
took beautiful sunset pictures on one of the islands
Mallory Square at Key West like a carnival
Caribbean atmosphere making it seem more fun
ran into high school drama teacher who had failed me
street performers entertained the crowd
wonderful Key Lime pie

F. **In the following list of ideas generated for a paragraph about the <u>importance of preparing carefully in order for a vacation trip by car to be fun</u>, write a K for the details to keep for support and a D for those you would drop because they do not support your point.** *(counts as 5 test items)*

Topic sentence: If you prepare carefully, taking a family vacation trip in a car can be a success.

_____ look at a map carefully to learn about driving times between destinations

_____ plan to take along games the kids can play in the car

_____ take traveler's checks for greater security

_____ one time we drove only an hour and got in a traffic jam

_____ make sure the car is in good condition before you go

G. **Write two more possible support details for the above prewriting list.**

1.

2.

H. **Imagine that you are describing your room at home. Write one sentence of this description to include in a note to each of the following two possible audiences. Make sure your sentence matches the intended audience.**

1. Write one sentence about your room for a younger cousin who is coming to visit for a month and who expects to stay in your room (you <u>don't</u> want him/her to stay with you).

2. Someone you love has asked you to describe your room so that he or she can learn a bit more about you (he or she has never seen your room).

A. **In the following groups of ideas, circle the letter of the sentence that could serve as a topic sentence or thesis statement for the others.** *(Note: Although the scope of a paragraph is different from the scope of an essay, the main idea sentence for either one must make the topic clear and state a main point.)*

1. a. Aunt Maude has plants in every room of the house, even the bathroom.
   b. The ivy that covers her back porch was lovingly nurtured from its original 6" pot that started twenty-four years ago.
   c. My great-aunt's passion for gardening is evident everywhere in her home.
   d. Shelves in the living room are filled with books about gardens all over the world.
   e. There is always a vase of cut flowers from her yard on the kitchen table.

2. a. Rain filled the tents because they had not been put up properly.
   b. My family's camping trip was a disaster mainly due to our inexperience.
   c. When we arrived at our intended destination, the campground was full, and since we had not made reservations, we had to move on.
   d. No one had thought to bring dishwashing liquid or matches.
   e. The meal we tried to cook ended up being cold canned beans.

3. a. Burns can be classified as first, second, or third degree, according to the depth of the burn.
   b. First-degree burns are superficial and cause the skin to turn red.
   c. A deeper burn that splits the skin layers is a second-degree burn.
   d. Third-degree burns destroy all layers of skin and extend into deeper tissues.
   e. There are three kinds of burns.

4. a. My neighbor Mr. Sanders likes animals better than people.
   b. The grouchy man yells at children in his yard.
   c. Mr. Sanders buys steak for his four dogs.
   d. The woods behind his house are filled with feeders for birds and squirrels.
   e. He never speaks to neighbors or attends the community picnic.

5. a. Small TV screens are being installed in the back of the front-seat headrest so that passengers can be entertained on long trips.
   b. Engineers have designed a remote starter that can be used to start the car while the owner is inside his or her house.
   c. Hands-free cell phones make driving safer for those who must talk and drive.
   d. Cars are becoming "smarter" because of some new designs from automotive technology.
   e. A new product, called the Auto PC, is bringing the world to the car radio.

B. **In the blank beside each of the following sentences, write G if it is a good topic sentence or B if it is bad.**

1. _____ A good vacation must be carefully planned.

2. _____ In this paragraph, I will be sharing the reasons I quit high school.

3. ____ The local hospital has a great number of problems that need to be addressed.

4. ____ Support services to the evening students at this college could be improved with three simple changes.

5. ____ Last year, my mom and dad took a trip to British Columbia.

6. ____ Everyone should recycle to make this a better world.

7. ____ My high school swim team coach was an intimidating woman.

8. ____ Television is stupid sometimes, but radio is better.

9. ____ The winning team scored seven touchdowns last night.

10. ____ Central Park in New York City has a variety of activities for visitors to enjoy.

11. ____ Mike has taken two steps to reduce his agoraphobia, his fear of being in a crowd.

12. ____ The child care system has a lot of things to recommend it.

C. **Read each of the following paragraphs, and then from the choices below, choose the best option for a topic sentence. Circle the letter of your choice.**

1. _____. For example, the money in both England and Ireland was called "pounds" although the two did not have the same exchange rate when changing from U.S. dollars. Likewise, visitors had to figure Swiss francs and French francs, which also had totally different values compared to the dollar. The use of the euro, a common currency throughout Europe, has made traveling between countries easier for tourists.
   a. Europe's money is different from that in the United States.
   b. Changing money as a tourist in Western Europe used to be rather challenging.
   c. A trip to Europe requires the tourist to change dollars into foreign currency.

2. _____. The downtown streets in the oldest area of downtown Boston, unlike those of New York or Washington, D.C., are not on a grid running north and south, east and west. Rather, they wander crazily at odd angles. There is a story that seventeenth century cow paths influenced the layout of the streets. As cows were led to Boston Common to graze, their haphazard loops created the maze of streets. As the town grew, the paths were turned into the streets of today.
   a. Boston is one of the oldest cities in the United States.
   b. History is sometimes evident in the present in such cities as Boston.
   c. Finding one's way around Boston, Massachusetts, can be a challenge due to the unusual layout of the city streets.

D. **The following are attempts to write main idea sentences, either topic sentences for paragraphs or thesis statements for an essay. Under each one, there are four choices. Circle the letter of the choice that you think best describes the most appropriate application for the sentence.**

1. The first hour of my daily routine is the same every day.
   a. too narrow for meaningful development
   b. appropriate for a paragraph's topic sentence
   c. appropriate for an essay's thesis statement
   d. too broad for meaningful development

2. My mother's period of critical illness taught me three important lessons that will stay with me forever.
   a. too narrow for meaningful development
   b. appropriate for a paragraph's topic sentence
   c. appropriate for an essay's thesis statement
   d. too broad for meaningful development

3. The average temperature in Philadelphia in June is 83 degrees.
   a. too narrow for meaningful development
   b. appropriate for a paragraph's topic sentence
   c. appropriate for an essay's thesis statement
   d. too broad for meaningful development

4. Romance causes joy and heartache.
   a. too narrow for meaningful development
   b. appropriate for a paragraph's topic sentence
   c. appropriate for an essay's thesis statement
   d. too broad for meaningful development

E. **In each of the following sentences, underline the limited topic once and double underline the controlling idea or specific point the writer is making about the topic.**

   1. superintendent in my apartment building, Ms. Layton, treats all of us residents as she would her own children.

   2. My daughter's first piano lesson was a joy because of her wonderful teacher.

A. **In the following groups of ideas, circle the letter of the sentence that could serve as a topic sentence or thesis statement for the others.** *(Note: Although the scope of a paragraph is different from the scope of an essay, the main idea sentence for either one must make the topic clear and state a main point.)*

1. a. The fabric of his curtains and comforter has a sports theme.
    b. All over the walls, there are posters of his favorite team, the Dolphins.
    c. Mike built the headboard of his bed to look like goalposts.
    d. The floor is covered with green carpet that looks like Astroturf.
    e. My cousin Mike's room reveals to any visitor that he is a football fanatic.

2. a. You'll want to start with a refrigerated roll-out dough, which is fairly cheap.
    b. Making your own pizza at home is easy and economical.
    c. Look for toppings from among the leftovers in your refrigerator.
    d. Some really tasty sauces come in a can or a jar, and you can add extra spices.
    e. Cover your custom pizza with cheese, and bake it until the sauce bubbles.

3. a. The first half-hour after the standard call is usually spent getting made up.
    b. There is a company meeting for announcements an hour before the play begins.
    c. Actors must signal their arrival backstage by signing the call board.
    d. Actors at our college theater follow a routine before the curtain rises.
    e. The last bit of preparation is the physical and vocal warm-up period.

4. a. Tuyet has told us somber stories of her challenges after leaving Vietnam.
    b. An African student who earned a master's degree in Nigeria has shared how frustrating it is to be treated as an uneducated person.
    c. The international students in my psychology class have made the discussions more interesting.
    d. We have heard some varied strong opinions about the role of women in the world of work.
    e. The professor has done an excellent job of encouraging international students to express their views.

5. a. For one thing, playing tennis keeps him in good physical shape.
    b. My dad's weekly tennis game gives him several kinds of rewards.
    c. Dad is very competitive, and playing against excellent players helps him improve his game.
    d. Perhaps the greatest benefit of all is the social interaction he enjoys.
    e. Dad looks forward to his weekly game so much that the anticipation itself is fun.

B. **In the blank beside each of the following sentences, write G if it is a good topic sentence or B if it is bad.**

1. _____ I think that sororities and fraternities have some good qualities.

2. _____ Volunteering at the local soup kitchen has taught me to be gracious in giving.

3. ____ In 1896, the U.S. government bought the house where Lincoln died.

4. ____ My younger brother has a pet iguana that requires special care.

5. ____ The ice storm we endured last winter brought us closer together as a family.

6. ____ The way the elected officials behave in some cities is disgraceful.

7. ____ Awareness of how you actually spend your study time can lead you to use it more effectively.

8. ____ Math is a required course in most college programs.

9. ____ Some TV shows have affected children in very intense ways.

10. ____ I had to learn the hard way never to buy a used car from a friend.

11. ____ Brandi's job as a firefighter is rewarding to her.

12. ____ Hong Kong is one of the largest cities in the world.

C. **Read each of the following paragraphs carefully, and then choose the best option for a topic sentence. Circle the letter of your choice.**

1. _____. She has to have her special chair as well as a big towel to lie down on. Then, of course, there's the necessary cooler with drinks and snacks. Her huge beach bag bulges with magazines, a headset, five or six bottles of sunscreen, and an extra towel or two. If her kids are with her, she has buckets and pails and all their gear, too. It looks like too much trouble; if I were Alice, I might just head out to the back yard.
   a. My friend Alice is determined to get a sun tan and relax at the beach.
   b. Going to the beach for the day can be one of summer's joys for Alice.
   c. Alice looks like a pack horse when she's loaded down for a day at the beach.

2. _____. That was the time of evening when it was just becoming too dark to see the softball, so we kids would stop playing and gather on Charlie's front steps. We loved to unwind from the day, talking about the good things that had happened and planning more adventures for the next day. When we weren't acting too grown up, we would even catch lightning bugs during this sweet twilight hour. As it got darker, we would watch the lights fill the skyline across the bay until our moms called us home. The ritual ending of the day is one of my most valuable memories from childhood.
   a. I grew up in a small town across from a city on the bay.
   b. As a child, I loved the ending of the day of summer play at twilight.
   c. My childhood was filled with tender moments spent with my buddies.

D. **The following are attempts to write main idea sentences, either topic sentences for paragraphs or thesis statements for an essay. Under each one, there are four choices. Circle the letter of the choice that you think best describes the scope of the sentence.**

1. Food is the basis of life for living beings, both plant and animal.
   a. too narrow for meaningful development
   b. appropriate for a paragraph's topic sentence
   c. appropriate for an essay's thesis statement
   d. too broad for meaningful development

2. My grandmother's old farmhouse is a delightful array of smells, colors, and textures.
   a. too narrow for meaningful development
   b. appropriate for a paragraph's topic sentence
   c. appropriate for an essay's thesis statement
   d. too broad for meaningful development

3. My former neighbor Kelly went to college in Cleveland, Ohio.
   a. too narrow for meaningful development
   b. appropriate for a paragraph's topic sentence
   c. appropriate for an essay's thesis statement
   d. too broad for meaningful development

4. I spent an exciting afternoon last weekend at the women's golf tournament.
   a. too narrow for meaningful development
   b. appropriate for a paragraph's topic sentence
   c. appropriate for an essay's thesis statement
   d. too broad for meaningful development

E. **In each of the following sentences, underline the limited topic once and double underline the controlling idea (the specific point the writer is making about the topic).**

1. Studying in the upstairs reading room of the library is pointless because of the constant socializing that goes on in there.

2. Tina's three teenaged sons have very different personalities.

A. **Read each set of details that follow the topic sentences below. In each group, there is one idea that is not in unity. Cross through one idea that interferes with unity.**

1. Several children at the arts festival showed good business sense by making their own creations to sell.
    copper wire bent to make photo holders
    the festival had a zip line over the lake to drop kids to swim
    luminaries for candles made out of coffee cans
    clear handmade soap with a plastic bug inside

2. Learning how to take advantage of public transportation was not an easy task for a guy from the country.
    had to get schedules from the Transit Authority for buses and trains
    had to figure out how to use the fare card machines
    had to buy some good walking shoes
    had to interpret signs in the stations in order to change trains

3. The wedding was a beautiful occasion.
    Lin and Freddie had been dating for four years
    fresh spring flowers adorned every table
    a water fountain in the center of the park where the reception took place
    a rainbow was waiting when they came out of the chapel to the park

4. The balcony outside of my bedroom is a great place to write in my journal.
    comfortable chair with a wide arm to set journal on
    faces away from the street on to a large, peaceful back yard
    family knows not to bother me when I'm out there
    the balcony was added to the house in 1987

B. **For development, add a suitable detail to each of the following sets of ideas below. You may write from your own experience or use your imagination, but be sure your addition supports the topic sentence.**

1. I have good reasons never to eat in that restaurant again.
    poor service
    high prices

    _____

2. One of the most popular boys in my high school class was a real cut-up.
    teased the cheerleaders
    pretended to need crutches

    _____

3. Several people in my family have taught me by their example that hard work really pays off.

    Uncle Harold built his dry cleaning business into a franchise
    Mom went back to college at age 49 and graduated with honors

    _____

4. Babysitting for a neighbor's five kids when I was teenager convinced me to wait until I was older to have a child of my own.

    no time to enjoy my own books or TV programs
    always someone screaming for help or attention

    _____

C. Each of the following main idea sentences is followed by two attempts at details for development. Circle the letter of the choice that provides the more specific support.

1. My friend set me up with the worst blind date I have ever had.
   a. The young woman I went out with was silly and thoughtless of others.
   b. The young woman giggled nonstop and made insulting remarks about our waiter.

2. The prices that my neighbors put on their yard sale items were ridiculous.
   a. They were charging three dollars for a bent egg beater.
   b. They were charging too much for out-of-date and unusable kitchen items.

3. Our new puppy has made the house a mess.
   a. He destroys everything he can find and gets into places where he doesn't belong.
   b. He completely demolished my bedroom shoes, and he nearly suffocated when he climbed into the blanket chest.

4. The shopping mall near my home is a great place to find unusual gifts.
   a. One booth sells leather goods from Arizona, and another features blueberry jam packaged in handmade pottery, both from Maine.
   b. A shopper can buy many kinds of household items made all over the country.

D. Arrange the following scrambled list of sentences for a paragraph in a coherent order. Write the number 1 beside the topic sentence, the one that all the others support. Then number the other sentences, starting with what seems to be the least important reason and ending with the most important. Pay attention to transition words to help you arrange the sentences.

1. _____ First, Ernesto was really getting tired of spending an hour and a half on the road every day.
   _____ Most importantly, however, was the way his job was affecting his health.
   _____ Ernesto decided to change jobs for several reasons.
   _____ The fumes were aggravating his allergies and causing terrible headaches.
   _____ Moreover, his third shift hours interfered with taking classes in the morning, when more options are available.

E. Add transitional words to improve coherence in the following two sentences.

1. For years, Jill had planned on majoring in dance at the university. _____, she changed her mind when her part time job showed her how much she loved working with children. _____, she intends to major in early childhood education.

2. Toddlers often explore their surroundings and pick up things within reach, often investigating them by putting them into their mouths. _____, a careful parent must put dangerous items out of reach of a curious child. _____, the floor should be clear of pins, tacks, or other sharp items.

F. In the following passage, the topic sentence has two key words underlined. Circle the words in the rest of the paragraph that reinforce these ideas and therefore add to the paragraph's coherence. Look for repetitions of key words, pronouns, and transitional words. Circle at least seven words.

My great-grandmother was a very resourceful woman. She lived in a remote area of the mountains and raised seven children. Grandma's husband died when her youngest child was only eleven months old, and from that time, she had to find means to feed her large family. She found these supplies mostly on the land. For one thing, she had a wonderful green thumb. This remarkable woman could grow better vegetables than many more experienced farmers. Grandma also knew the secrets to digging medicinal herbs and roots that she could take to the one local store to trade for things she couldn't grow. Furthermore, Grandma was resourceful in finding ways to stretch the small amount of money she earned sewing for neighbors. For example, she would wear acorns on her dresses instead of buttons. I would like to think that I have just a fraction of my great-grandmother's ability to meet any situation with resourceful confidence.

G. Read the following two paragraphs, labeled a and b.

a. When my mom was in the hospital last year, her sister, my aunt Lou, helped us out. As a single mother, Mom has always had her hands full with us four children, and Lou stepped in to carry on with our daily needs. She stayed at our house for six weeks, made breakfast and bag lunches every morning, and got the two middle kids ready for me to drop off at school on my way to the college. Every day, Lou made two dishes for supper; she served one for dinner and put the other in the freezer for later. The best meal she ever made, in my opinion, was her Hawaiian chicken casserole. Lou drove my brothers around to their sports activities, and helped them with homework in the evenings. She even managed to mend some of the clothes Mom had piled up. I don't know how we'd have managed without her.

b. My friend Janet's dad enjoys his life more than any other retired person I know. Mr. Hughes stays busy all the time, and he keeps a smile on his face. There's often a useful project or two going on in his workshop, and he volunteers for the community. He maintains most of his usual activities with his church, too. Her dad retired after twenty-eight years with the same textile business. In addition, Mr. Hughes has more time for his many hobbies now. Always an avid sportsman, he participates in his favorite sports; moreover, he keeps up with them on TV. He has the right kind of attitude to make the most of his well-deserved leisure time. I hope I can remember Mr. Hughes when I am ready to retire and model my later years after his.

1. Which paragraph is better developed, a or b? _____

2. Each of the above paragraphs has one sentence that is not in unity with the controlling idea (main point) of the paragraph. In each paragraph, cross out the sentence that disrupts unity.

A. **Read each set of details that follow the topic sentences below. In each group, there is one idea that is not in unity. Cross through the idea that interferes with unity.**

1. State budget cuts have required college officials to reduce expenses and services.
   fewer part-time faculty, resulting in larger classes
   bookstore doesn't keep as many hours on the weekend
   tuition was kept at the same cost as last year
   grounds not maintained as well due to reduction in staff

2. Jaime and Sonia have a small apartment, but they use their limited space well.
   a closet under the stairwell holds cleaning supplies and linens
   Jaime built shelves all the way to the ceiling along one wall of the bedroom
   they pack out-of-season clothes in cedar boxes under the bed
   the extra bedroom set they aren't using is stored in Sonia's mother's garage

3. Using less water on a daily basis is not so hard to do if you develop a few new habits.
   turn off the water while you brush your teeth
   drinking water with meals is healthier for you than drinking other beverages
   put a plastic bottle in the toilet tank to make it use less water
   use your old dishwater to water house plants

4. Americans are learning to appreciate sports other than the traditional mainstream ones.
   baseball is gaining great popularity in Japan
   soccer, more widespread in Europe and South America, is big with kids
   many universities offer lacrosse scholarships
   Americans love to watch the gymnastic events at the Olympics

B. **For development, add a suitable detail to each of the following sets of ideas below. You may write from your own experience or use your imagination, but be sure your addition supports the topic sentence.**

1. When I was young, I enjoyed all kinds of strenuous, challenging activities.
   learned to rappel off a mountain at age twelve
   played one-on-one basketball with my older sister's team
   _____

   The surprise party we gave my aunt was a huge success.
   there were guests who had flown in from four different states
   the catering service was excellent
   _____

3. Growing up on a farm requires a person to become accustomed to regular chores.
   the cows must be milked about the same time each morning
   crops have to be picked clean often so they will keep bearing
   _____

4. Although we were exhausted, we were proud as we looked over our accomplishments.
we had painted the walls in the bedroom
we had moved all the furniture out of the living room

_____

C. Each of the following main idea sentences is followed by two attempts at details for development. Circle the letter of the choice that provides more specific support.

1. Ricky was a daredevil who never really grew up.
   a. Today he still likes to take risks and has an unconventional job.
   b. Today he is a pilot for a hot air balloon that flies for a local TV station.

2. Aunt Frances is an extremely superstitious person.
   a. She will not go out of the house on a Friday the 13th or walk under a ladder.
   b. She has a lot of unfounded fears that she has talked herself into.

3. Although Americans and the British both speak English, they use different vocabulary.
   a. Common everyday items are named different things, for example.
   b. An American uses an "elevator" to get to her "apartment" while an Englishman uses the "lift" to get to his "flat."

4. The committee faces several important decisions regarding the new building.
   a. Provisions for adequate classrooms and labs must be made.
   b. The committee must approve the size, layout, and location of classrooms.

D. Arrange the following scrambled list of sentences for a paragraph in a coherent order. Write the number 1 beside the topic sentence, the one that all the others support. Then number the other sentences, starting with what seems to be the least important reason and ending with the most important. Pay attention to transition words to help you arrange the sentences.

_____ I hit the snooze alarm at least twice before I manage to get up about 7:05.

_____ My typical day begins about the same way every day.

_____ Once I'm finally up, I rush through my bathroom ritual and throw on some clothes.

_____ I begin my long, busy day by reaching for the ringing clock.

_____ I arrive at work at 8:00, ready to maintain a fast pace all day.

_____ Breakfast, usually a piece of toast with peanut butter, is eaten in the car.

E. Add transitional words to improve coherence in the following two sentences.

1. The campsite where my family spent our last vacation was totally unsuitable.
   _____, the location was inconvenient, up a long hill from the bathrooms.
   _____, there were so many bugs and loud bullfrogs that we couldn't sleep.

2. Washing my dog is an exercise in patience. _____, I have to round up little Phoebe who runs when she sees her bathtub being hauled out. _____, it's a challenge keeping her from trailing soapy water all over the house.

F. In the following passage, the topic sentence has several key words underlined. Circle the words in the rest of the paragraph that help to reinforce these ideas and thus achieve coherence. Look for repetitions of key words, synonyms, and transitional words. Circle at least seven words.

As a teenager, the first real goal I ever set for myself was to overcome my shyness. I was a lonely and unhappy person, mainly because I was too shy to initiate conversation and too withdrawn for many people to reach out to. Too timid to join clubs, I went straight home after school and avoided classmates. When I got a C in English, which was my favorite subject, only because I was too introverted to give a required oral report, I knew I needed to make some changes to conquer this problem. I gave myself a pep talk and set out my long term goal: to join a club before the end of the school year. First, I started with the a strategy designed to help me meet that goal. I talked to the school counselor about my shyness, my determination to change, and possible extracurricular activities. She advised me to join the newspaper staff, since I enjoyed writing. Working on the newspaper staff helped me overcome some of my shyness; I often had to interview people for the stories I wrote. Furthermore, my focus was on the story instead of myself. I learned that by taking one step toward my goal at a time, I could move toward success.

G. Read the following two paragraphs, labeled a and b, and answer the questions.

a. My high school gym teacher was the most intimidating man I ever met. Standing six-feet-five and weighing at least 250 pounds, he looked like a Mr. Universe contestant. From his large shaved head to his size 13 feet, he was always in motion. Coach's small eyes were like radar, burning a hole in the most timid of students. Physical education had actually been my favorite subject until I found myself in his class in the tenth grade. His crooked smile seemed to sneer aloud at us. What scared me most was his voice. It was like a foghorn when he yelled at us to keep up the pace during laps and basketball drills. This bear of a man had a way of making us feel that he was watching each one of us exclusively, which was, of course, impossible. It was a workout to watch him watching us.

b. The project that the Dental Hygienists Club on campus recently undertook taught us some valuable lessons about human nature. The project involved working with the children that are cared for in our childcare program in the afternoons after school. We were helping them learn about dental care. Children need to develop hygiene habits at an early age in order to carry them throughout their lives. Hoping to learn about why children develop a fear of dentists, we came up with several ways to help the children with their routine teeth care. Not only did we learn about their feelings, we also found out about the kind of patience that is required to work with children on a regular basis. We observed how their feelings influence each other, too. The club advisor guided us in writing a summary of our findings.

©2004 by Prentice Hall. PEARSON EDUCATION, INC.

1. Which paragraph is better developed, a or b? _____

2. Each of the above paragraphs has one sentence that is not in unity with the controlling idea (main point) of the paragraph. In each paragraph, cross out that sentence that disrupts unity.

A. Read paragraph 1. The writer of paragraph 2 intended to copy paragraph 1 exactly, but he or she made six mistakes. Circle each spot in which paragraph 2 is different from 1.

1. My best friend's mother-in-law is the only person I know who has a realistic dummy of a man to ride with her in her car for safety purposes. Mrs. Baker calls her companion Hercules. I haven't actually met Hercules, but I would like to someday because of the tales I have heard about him. For one thing, according to my friend, he has had more than one scrape with the law. Once, when Hercules was in the back seat, apparently taking a nap, a policeman stopped Mrs. Baker to find out if she was transporting a criminal. Another time, his hand was sticking out of the trunk, and Mrs. Baker was thought to be a murderer. Several of Mrs. Baker's friends have been startled when they thought a man was staring at them from the car. They thought he looked rather intent on studying their actions. Hercules looks so real that he has fooled many an innocent onlooker. I hope to soon see this marvel for myself!

2. My best friend's mother-in law is the only person I know who has a realistic dummy of a man to ride with her in her car for safety purposes. Mrs. Baker calls her companion Hercules. I have'nt actually met Hercules, but I would like to someday because of the tales I have heard about him. For one thing, according to my friend he has had more than one scrape with the law. Once, when Hercules was in the back seat, apparently taking a nap, a policeman stopped Mrs. Baker to find out if she was transporting a criminal. Another time his hand was sticking out of the trunk, and Mrs. Baker was thought to be a murderess. Several of Mrs. Baker's friend have been startled when they thought a man was staring at them from the car. They thought he looked rather intent on studying their actions. Hercules looks so real that he has fooled many an inocent onlooker. I hope to soon see this marvel for myself!

B. Proofread the following paragraph to determine where words have been unnecessarily repeated or omitted or where there are wrong word errors. Cross through extra words. Insert omitted words above the line. Circle and correct word mistakes. You should find six mistakes.

Jerry is a baseball fanatic. He loves playing the game, watching the game, and talking about the game. Jerry can quote almost any player's batting average or error stats—and not not just the current players, but also those from throughout history. This baseball fan's ideal of a vacation is to go Florida, not for enjoying the beach or Disneyworld, but to catch six or eight games during a week of spring training. Jerry even has a fantasy team with several other baseball lovers. This is league of pretend teams, each of which has a regular lineup of players from real life, only put into different groupings for the fantasy team. On Jerry's wedding day, a buddy of his called up to ask if he could trade a player. Jerry actually past up a chance to get a great player and asked him to call back the next day! This is the only the time I can recall that Jerry didn't put baseball first.

C. **Read the following paragraph carefully, looking for mistakes in sentence structure (run-on, comma splice, fragment, modifier placement) and grammar (agreement, adverb form). There are seven errors that need correcting. Cross through errors, and write your corrections above the line.**

Charlotte, a neighbor of mine who is real energetic, recently returned from an educational trip with Habitat for Humanity the purpose of the trip was to build two new houses for families whose homes had been destroyed by flooding. Charlotte feels that she received more than she gave through this project. Because she learned so much about the work involved and how to be a part of a team. Charlotte, an inexperienced carpenter, was the only woman on the framing crew. Each worker on the team had their own assignments. Charlotte learned how to use a level and a nail gun, tools that was essential on the job. After breakfast at 6:30, the crew was hammering by 7:00 a.m., workers took half an hour for a lunch break and kept working until 5:30. Working at this pace for a week, nine walls and over twenty roof trusses were built by Charlotte's team. When she got home, Charlotte called to tell me how tired but pleased she was with her work.

D. **Read the following draft of a paragraph. There are errors in unity and coherence (organization) that could be corrected by omitting one sentence and rearranging some others. First, cross through the sentence that needs to be omitted. Then, underline the topic sentence. Finally, insert numbers near the beginning of the remaining four sentences to renumber them as support points 1, 2, 3, and 4.**

Different environments result in different flavors of coffee. Not many coffee lovers know much about the plant that ends up as the drink that starts so many mornings. Almost eighty countries have these characteristics and have large coffee plantations. The coffee shrub requires a frost-free climate, moderate rainfall, and a lot of sunshine. My favorite coffee is from Costa Rica, where there are many large coffee farms. The most special and therefore expensive coffees in the world come from the trees grown at high altitudes in the tropics, often on volcanic soil.

A.   **Read paragraph 1. The writer of paragraph 2 intended to copy paragraph 1 exactly, but he or she made six mistakes. Circle each spot in which paragraph 2 is different from 1.**

1. One of my favorite memories is of a weekend spent with two of my childhood friends on Block Island. Block Island is located off the coast of Rhode Island, not far from Long Island. It is a beautiful island of cliffs high above the sea. One of the activities we enjoyed was bicycling around the perimeter. The hills were tough, but the scenery was worth it. One of my friends knew someone with a boat who took us out to Black Rock where we swam and snorkeled around the base of the rock. Nearby was a wreck of a ship lying about twenty feet down; the water was so clear that we could float on top and see all the way down. Finally, we enjoyed exploring the quaint New England town at the harbor. The weekend on Block Island was magic: good weather, beautiful scenery, precious company, and nature's gifts. I will always cherish this memory.

2. One of my favorite memories is of a weekend spent with two of my childhood freinds on Block Island. Block Island is located off the coast of Rhode Island not far from Long Island. It is a beautiful island of cliffs high above the sea. One of the activities we enjoyed was bicycling around the perimeter. The hills were tough, but the scenery was worth it. One of my friends knows someone with a boat who took us out to Black rock where we swam and snorkeled around the base of the rock. Nearby was a wreck of a ship lying about twenty feet down, the water was so clear that we could float on top and see all the way down. Finally, we enjoyed exploring the quaint New England town at the harbor. The weekend on Block Island was magic: good weather, beautiful scenery, precious company, and natures' gifts. I will always cherish this memory.

B.   **Proofread the following paragraph to determine where words have been unnecessarily repeated or omitted or where there are wrong word errors. Cross through extra words. Insert omitted words above the line. Circle and correct word mistakes. You should find six mistakes.**

At my husband's recent community college graduation ceremony, I learned something new while reading the program. It's not that I was bored; I just tried entertain myself after his name was called and all those other students marched across the stage to receive there diplomas. At the back of the program, there was a lists of the meanings of the colors on the faculty members' hoods. A person who has a Master's degree wears a hood on his or her gown, and this hood has two stripes: one for for the university attended and the other for the subject area. For example, a white stripe signifies a degree in arts or humanities. An orange one stands for engineering. Golden yellow means science, and light blue means education. I spent several long moment looking at the faculty members, trying to figure out what they teach. It helped pass the time until I could congratulate my husband with hug.

C. **Read the following paragraph carefully, looking for mistakes in sentence structure (run-on, comma splice, fragment, modifier placement) and grammar (agreement, adverb form). There are six errors that need correcting. Cross through errors, and write your corrections above the line.**

Yesterday morning at the local diner, I had an interesting encounter that taught me a lesson about my own prejudice. Since I was eating alone, I sat at the counter, that way, I wouldn't take up a table in the crowded little restaurant. I am a regular there, so the server soon brought me some coffee and my usual breakfast. Two eggs over easy, bacon, hashbrowns, and wheat toast. As I begun to eat, a neatly dressed woman sat down next to me. She ordered breakfast and started to read a book. Not recognizing her, I figured that she was a visitor and perhaps a bit shy I spoke up to welcome her, telling her she'd found the best breakfast spot in the area. After a great conversation about her book, a travelogue of America's national parks, I just knew she had to be a teacher. I was so wrong. One of the biggest surprises of my life were finding out that this petite, intelligent lady was a truck driver for a large company hauling electronics across the country. I had thought that all truck drivers were uneducated rednecks, my new friend showed me not to stereotype anyone. It was a great lesson to start my day.

D. **Read the following draft of a paragraph. There are errors in unity and coherence (organization) that could be corrected by omitting one sentence and rearranging some others. First, cross through the sentence that needs to be omitted. Then underline the topic sentence. Then insert numbers near the beginning of the remaining five sentences to renumber them as support points 1, 2, 3, 4, and 5.**

College can be a real challenge for many people. It may be quick and convenient to eat junk food, but the lack of nutrition will catch up with a person who habitually eats poorly. In the high stress world of college, students should take special care to stay physically fit. One way to do this is to eat wisely. Another concern is getting enough exercise to offset the sedentary hours spent in class and studying. Finally, a wise student will pay attention to keeping as regular a schedule as possible and getting adequate sleep. A brisk walk or game of pick-up basketball can do wonders for the attention span.

A. **Circle T for true or F for false for each one of the following statements.**

T F 1. A writer should tell all of the possible items in a category when giving examples.

T F 2. The topic sentence of an illustration paragraph should make clear what the writer intends to give examples <u>of</u>.

T F 3. Well-chosen examples are those that fit the point the writer is trying to make.

B. **Read each of the following pairs of topics for a paragraph or an essay. Which of the two would be more suited to development by examples? Circle the letter of your choice.**

1. a. Specialty kitchen tools used in baking
    b. The Eighteenth Amendment to the Constitution

2. a. Strict teachers that I didn't appreciate until later in life
    b. Why I decided to major in nursing

3. a. A humorous TV commercial for a local bowling alley
    b. Sources of protein other than meat

4. a. My favorite author of books for children
    b. Responsibilities involved in owning a pet

C. **In each of the following, circle the letter of the better main idea sentence to develop by giving examples.**

1. a. My son's proudest moment was accepting his "Most Improved Soccer Player" award.
    b. I have a few friends whose crazy antics can cheer me up when I'm down.

2. a. Many words in the English language can be used in more than one context to mean different things.
    b. The cold I had last winter was the worst one I have ever had.

3. a. Jenna has collected several kinds of political artifacts, each from a different country.
    b. The closer a place is to the equator, the more constant is its climate throughout the year.

4. a. The *Titanic* sank in the mid-Atlantic in 1912 on her first voyage.
    b. Several popular movies deal with events from history.

D. **For each of the phrases below, an example is given. In the blank, add another example.**

1. Hand tools in a typical carpenter's toolbox
    a. hammer
    b. _____

F. Supply transitional words that will help make the following samples from illustration writing more coherent. Use a different transitional word in the two items that follow.

1. Sherry is the most self-disciplined person I know. _____, she keeps herself on a strict budget and balances her checkbook to the penny.

2. Russell loves having his kids on the weekends, but sometimes their desire to be doing something every minute wears him out. One recent weekend, all three of them wanted him to drive over to different friends' houses to visit and play. _____, they begged him to take them to the park, to the mall, and to the school track.

G. Read the following illustration paragraph and answer the questions that follow.

My grandmother's generosity is one of her most endearing qualities. She is also very unselfish. One gift she gives freely is her resources. Although she is not rich, she is eager to share what she has, and she doesn't expect favors in return. For example, when I was short of funds last term, Grandma gave me enough money to buy my last two textbooks. She also loaned me her car to use for a week while mine was in the shop. Another area of her generosity is time and talent. Grandma sends me homemade cookies and brownies that are so delicious I have to hide them from my friends. Whenever I visit, she asks if I have laundry to do or any clothes to mend, and she sends me home with everything clean and folded. As much as I appreciate all this, I have to say that the best gift of Grandma's generosity is her love. She listens well and offers wise advice when I ask for it. Her affection is evident, and her unconditional acceptance is a gift I depend on. My grandmother exemplifies the spirit of generosity.

1. What is the writer providing examples <u>of</u>?

_____

2. What are three main examples provided in this paragraph?

_____   _____   _____

3. Write here one additional supporting detail that might belong in this paragraph.

_____

4. Cross out the one sentence that does not belong in this paragraph because it repeats unnecessarily.

4. a. Amy's love of Southwestern America is evident in her newly decorated kitchen.
   b. Julie has the same eating habits as those she had when she was five years old.

D. For each of the phrases below, an example is given. In the blank, add another example.

1. A deceased former President of the USA
   a. Franklin D. Roosevelt
   b. _____

2. A popular vacation city west of the Mississippi River
   a. Las Vegas, Nevada
   b. _____

3. Evidence that a person did not have enough sleep the night before
   a. frequent yawning
   b. _____

4. An achievement that makes one's family proud
   a. graduation from high school
   b. _____

E. For each phrase below, there is a list. Circle the letter of the item in each list that is NOT an example of the phrase.

1. Complaints about an unpopular teacher
   a. gives lectures that are long and boring
   b. uses vocabulary that is too difficult
   c. got degree from a prestigious Ivy League university
   d. insults anyone who needs help

2. Features of a large grocery store that make it convenient for one-stop shopping
   a. It has a large produce section with imported vegetables.
   b. It has a counter for buying postage stamps and weighing mail.
   c. It has a pharmacy and health food department.
   d. It is near a drive-through dry-cleaning service.

3. Unusual pets
   a. Pot-bellied pig
   b. Iguana
   c. Snake
   d. Dog

4. Signs that my friend Bert is dependable
   a. He shows up at the time he says he will.
   b. He uses his common sense in accomplishing tasks.
   c. He finishes any job he undertakes.
   d. He always keeps secrets confidential when asked to do so.

A.　Circle the letter of the choice that best completes or describes the following sentences.

1. Developing a paragraph or an essay by giving examples means that the writer provides
   a. concrete, specific illustrations of something
   b. reasons for something
   c. information about types of something

2. Examples are not effective when they
   a. are numerous enough to give the reader a clear idea of something
   b. relate to the main point expressed in the topic sentence or thesis statement
   c. include so few details that the reader must guess or use his or her imagination

3. An example is not the same as a synonym.
   a. the above sentence is true
   b. the above sentence is false

B.　Read each of the following pairs of topics for a paragraph or an essay. Which of the two would be more suited to development by examples? Circle the letter of your choice.

1. a. Services for the elderly in this town
   b. Changing a flat tire

2. a. The best book you ever read
   b. Natural disasters

3. a. How large whales can grow in size
   b. Qualities that make a good roommate

4. a. Ways to make money working at home
   b. The part of a stereo speaker that allows for clarity of sound

C.　In each of the following, circle the letter of the better main idea sentence to develop by giving examples.

1. a. The intense sadness I felt at leaving my hometown a year ago really surprised me.
   b. The homeless man's erratic actions and words revealed his unsettled state of mind.

2. a. The city employs workers in many areas to improve the safety and quality of life here.
   b. One student in my sociology class rarely does her homework or participates in class.

3. a. Mosquitoes and hot weather make summer my least favorite time of year.
   b. Several changes in my family life have led me to seek additional training in business.

2. As I entered the school office, I saw the principal of my middle school glaring at me. _____ him, I could see my parents' upset faces.

H. Read the following description paragraph and answer the questions that follow.

To my ten-year-old wandering eyes, the office where my aunt worked as the director of a nature center was a magical place. To the left of the door, which was painted to look like petrified rock, was a huge aquarium filled with red, yellow, and purple fish and tall waving ferns. Beside it, in the corner, a mobile of the solar system hung, complete with a beanbag chair underneath, so I could sit and look up at the orbiting circles. Aunt Sandy had lived in Costa Rica, where she had even seen an active volcano, and she loved all kinds of nature. The window on that left wall looked out on the petting zoo with its sheep and goats. On the wall across from the door, my aunt had a desk, the top of which was covered with strange rocks and pieces of wood. Above her desk, a narrow horizontal window made of different panes of stained glass, each one a different color of the spectrum, gave the room a magical glow. The best part of her office was the right wall where a family of skeletons hung, lined up in a glass case.

1. Underline the topic sentence, and within it, circle the word or words that relay the main impression.

2. What is the main order of organization used in this paragraph?

3. List here three transitional words or phrases that aid in making the paragraph coherent.

4. Cross out one sentence that is not in unity.

5. Write your own conclusion to this paragraph.

D. **For each of the next two questions, write your own list of three details that would support the overall main impression stated in the topic sentences.**

    1. One look inside Stacy's bedroom tells you that she loves water sports.

          _____

          _____

          _____

    2. The trail we hiked up was difficult, but the view at the top was worth it.

          _____

          _____

          _____

E. **Rewrite the following two topic sentences to improve them for the purpose of beginning a descriptive paragraph. You will need to add words and change general words to more specific ones.**

    1. The car's condition showed how its owner felt.

          _____

    2. Jorge's girlfriend looks unlike any other woman he has dated.

          _____

F. **Organize the supporting details in the next question so that they will be in a coherent order for a description. Number from 1 to 4, with number 1 being the detail you would write first.**

    Topic sentence: Stan's old truck looks like it belongs in a circus side show.
    ____ the bed has odd handmade side walls with zigzag cuts across the top
    ____ hanging across the back of the truck bed on the tailgate are tiny blue and orange lights
    ____ the front bumper and hood are painted to look like a smiling face
    ____ the cab of the pickup is covered with graffiti-like slogans, written in crooked writing

G. **Supply transitional words or phrases that will help make the following samples from description writing more coherent.**

    1. Branches of hardwood trees waved high above us as we walked on the trail. At eye level, the rhododendron bushes were in bloom. _____ them, small wildflowers lined the path.

A. Circle T for true or F for false for each of the following statements.

T F 1. A descriptive paragraph or essay will often be arranged in time order.

T F 2. The main idea sentence must give some overall or dominant impression that provides a reason the description is worth telling.

T F 3. Descriptive writing uses sensory language, modifiers, and comparisons.

B. Read each of the following pairs of topics for a paragraph or essay. Which of the two would be more suited to development by description? Circle the letter of your choice.

1. a. the art corner in your child's kindergarten classroom
   b. the way your child's teacher has helped your daughter overcome shyness

2. a. a protest in your community against a new development
   b. your first pet, a cat, which was an unusual mix of breeds

3. a. how your sister met her husband
   b. the small chapel where your sister was married

4. a. the jean jacket covered with political buttons that your uncle always wears
   b. your uncle's opinions about what the school system needs

5. a. the funniest joke your grandfather used to tell
   b. Grandpa's tackle box full of fishing lures

C. In the each of the following, circle the best description main idea sentence.

1. a. The screened-in porch on our old beach house is a comfortable spot for a nap.
   b. All Dan does on vacation is sit on the porch and read science fiction.

2. a. I am so tired of the junk mail I receive every day.
   b. Marcia's desk looks like a sales exhibit for a computer accessory store.

3. a. Taking care of a large flower garden can be time consuming.
   b. My friend Nelda's exercise room at home is perfectly suited to her needs.

4. a. The needlepoint pillow my grandmother gave me for graduation reminds me of her love for birds.
   b. Grandma tried to teach me to do needlepoint, but I was too impatient to learn.

5. a. The bus shelter where Tom waits every morning is covered with clever, thought-provoking graffiti.
   b. Our community needs to upgrade its public transportation services.

G. Supply transitional words that will help make the following samples from description writing more coherent.

1. At the front of the classroom sat a large old teacher's desk. _____ it, a nervous student stood reading her book report in a shaky voice.

2. _____ the large picture of my grandfather sits the red leather chair where he sat when he read us stories.

H. Read the following description paragraph and answer the questions that follow.

To my childhood sensibilities, my grandmother's small basement was a mysterious and somewhat scary place. From her warm, cozy little main floor, I had to go downstairs by way of a steep, dark, and narrow stairwell, which was barely eighteen inches wide. It turned a sharp corner halfway down, and from upstairs, it looked like the steps stopped in midair. The smell was damp and musty from the moisture downstairs. Moisture can get into the walls of a place and ruin the sheetrock. My feet would land downstairs on a floor that was earthy, with old boards spaced apart, the dank, rich dirt showing between them. Above the floor, the walls were not finished inside but showed lumpy mortar between exposed old bricks. Perpendicular to the outer walls of the room were shelves of green beans and tomatoes in old glass Bell jars, canned by Grandma's skilled hands. Light from the small windows near the low ceiling shone mysteriously off the many colorful jars. Still higher, looking up, I could see the pipes to the plumbing upstairs, which added to the strangeness when I was a child. Once I grew older, I loved going down to the basement to feel as if I was going back in time.

1. Underline the topic sentence, and within it, circle the word or words that relay the main impression.

2. What is the main order of organization used in this paragraph?

3. List here three transitional words or phrases that aid in making the paragraph coherent.

4. Cross out one sentence that is not in unity.

5. Write your own conclusion to this paragraph.

3. a. The sight of my uncle in his hospital room caused me to worry.
    b. Janice took a careless risk when she drove her dad's car without his consent.

4. a. By looking around her room, one could see that Consuelo loved horses.
    b. There are three reasons that Steve is determined to buy a new computer.

5. a. Lee and Ralph both love their jobs as pharmacist assistants.
    b. My eleventh grade English teacher always appeared neat, even fastidious.

D. For the next two questions, write your own list of three details that would support the overall main impression stated in each of the following topic sentences written for a descriptive paragraph.

1. The party decorations brightened the activity room of the nursing home.

    _____

    _____

    _____

2. Todd's car looks like it's ready for the junkyard.

    _____

    _____

    _____

E. Rewrite the following two topic sentences to improve them for beginning a descriptive paragraph. You will need to add words and change general words to specific ones.

1. The scene was very impressive.

    _____

2. The room showed the characteristics of its owner.

    _____

F. Organize the supporting details in the next question so that they will be in a coherent order for a description. Number from 1 to 4, with number 1 being the detail you would write first.

Topic Sentence: From my balcony, I could see people enjoying the beautiful seaside.
_____ several kids building a sand castle in a tidal pool near the incoming waves
_____ a sailboat far out on the horizon
_____ just under my balcony, a couple strolling arm in arm
_____ a family playing in the waist-deep water

A. **Circle the letter of the choice that best completes the following sentences.**

    1. When a writer describes, he or she is giving the reader details of what something or someone _____.
       a. means in relation to steps in accomplishing a task
       b. is like compared to something or someone else
       c. is like to the senses: sight, hearing, taste, smell, and touch

    2. Effective descriptive writing requires the use of ____.
       a. clear examples
       b. sharp, exact details
       c. logical reasons

    3. The most effective method for organizing details for a coherent descriptive paragraph or essay is usually ___ .
       a. spatial, or space order, putting details in order of where they are located
       b. importance, or climax order, putting details in order of least to most important
       c. chronological, or time order, putting details in order of when they occurred

B. **Read each of the following pairs of topics for a paragraph or an essay. Which of the two would be more suited to development by description? Circle the letter of your choice.**

    1. a. a hospital waiting room
       b. kinds of children's camps

    2. a. a person you know who is extremely conceited
       b. what you wear on the weekend to work in the yard

    3. a. how your dog tortures the neighbor's cat
       b. the tiny kitchen of your first apartment

    4. a. the Masons pin you inherited from your grandfather
       b. the most frightening movie you ever saw

    5. a. why you listen to your favorite radio station in the car
       b. the cluttered attic in your best friend's house

C. **In each of the following, circle the letter of the better description main idea sentence.**

    1. a. The front porch of the homey country restaurant was very welcoming.
       b. An athlete should show good sportsmanship whether he wins or loses.

    2. a. The financial aid counselor helped me to complete an application successfully.
       b. The record store clerk looks as if he has kept the tattoo industry in business.

F. Read the following narrative paragraph and answer the questions that follow.

My twelfth birthday was originally a disappointment that turned into my best birthday ever. For five or six months preceding the big day, I begged my parents for a certain new bicycle. I had seen one in a medium price range that I figured my folks could afford. I hinted and even pleaded outright, promising to do extra chores if I got it. Pointing out that the only bike I had ever had was a hand-me-down from my older brother, I showed them how rusted the frame was. Meanwhile, my brother was begging for a set of tires for the car he had bought. When my birthday finally came, my hopes were so high. Instead of the bicycle, though, I got a new shirt, a pair of sneakers, and an envelope. At first, I thought it was just a card, but it turned out to have enough money for the bike in it. It also contained five "contracts" for extra work around the house that I could do to earn enough money for a much nicer bicycle. My parents gave me the gift of upgrading from the bike I had settled for. I ended up getting a great new bicycle that I helped to buy with money I had earned myself.

1. Underline the topic sentence in the above narrative paragraph.

2. Circle any transitional word or phrase that is used for coherence.

3. Using a carat (^) and writing above the line, insert any one transitional word or phrase at a spot where it will improve coherence.

4. Cross out one sentence that is not in unity.

5. In your own words, write what you think is the writer's reason (or the point) for writing this narrative.

_____

4. a. I remember the first time I tried to give my dog Patton a bath.
   b. Tabitha wears her hair in a different style and color every week.

5. a. My first experience with academic failure was also my first experience with humility.
   b. Maureen will turn fifty next month, the same month she graduates from college.

D. For the next two questions, put the events below the topic sentence in the best order for a narrative. Number from 1 to 5, with the first event in the sequence labeled number 1.

1. <u>Topic sentence:</u> There's one classic story from my childhood that shows what it was like to grow up with my dad.

_____ There was a huge wolf, or so it seemed, standing on his hind legs growling at poor Jimmy.

_____ It was a typical Saturday morning, and we kids were watching cartoons.

_____ My brother Jimmy opened the door and immediately wailed in terror.

_____ When the doorbell rang loudly and persistently, Mom called for one of us kids to get the door.

_____ My dad then took off the mask and managed to catch his frightened son and eventually had us all laughing, even Jimmy.

2. <u>Topic sentence:</u> My earliest memory is a dim picture of events surrounding my sister's birth.

_____ When we got to her room and Mom held both my little sister and me, I thought things might not be so bad after all.

_____ Down the hall from Mom's room, we stopped and looked at the new babies before we went to her room.

_____ I was not sure I wanted anyone else in my life, and I was especially upset when my mother had to go to the hospital that rainy night.

_____ I can remember feeling slightly nervous the next day as Daddy took me, in my favorite yellow dress, to visit Mom in the hospital.

_____ I was only three years old and the center of my parents' lives before my sister was born.

E. Supply transitional words that will help make the following samples of narrative writing more coherent.

1. At 8:00 a.m., the boss announced a meeting of all the sales clerks to be held at noon. _____ then, I worried about whether we might soon be laid off.

2. Jade was walking slowly, window shopping and admiring the spring decorations when _____ a loud siren sounded.

3. _____ I was writing my psychology paper, a phone call interrupted my concentration.

4. Sally and Chuck were fixing dinner. _____, their kids were planning a surprise for their anniversary celebration.

A.   Circle T for true or F for false for each of the following statements.

T F 1. Narrative writing relays a story that is told to make a point.

T F 2. The most effective organizing principle to use in narrative writing is usually time order.

T F 3. Point of view and verb tense in an effective narration must change back and forth several times in order for a story to hold the reader's interest.

T F 4. Transitional words that control the pace of the story are useful in achieving coherence in a narrative.

B.   Read each of the following pairs of topics for a paragraph or an essay. Which of the two would be more suited to development by narration? Circle the letter of your choice.

1.   a. Grandpa's tale of the most disastrous fishing trip he ever took
     b. The four most common kinds of fish in Lake Otter

2.   a. How to make authentic Italian lasagna
     b. Cooking your first dinner together as husband and wife

3.   a. Consulting a mechanic before buying a used car
     b. The accident at work that caused you to lose a finger

4.   a. The worst tropical storm you ever endured
     b. Three people who prove that "Beauty is only skin deep"

5.   a. The flat tire that caused Tim to meet his future wife Melanie
     b. The use of rock music in television commercials

C.   In each of the following, circle the letter of the better narration main idea sentence.

1.   a. The search for my first job away from home was an educational journey.
     b. Vegetables are nutritious any way you eat them, but uncooked is best of all.

2.   a. The busy evening routine I observed as a patient taught me that a hospital is no place to get a decent night's sleep.
     b. An elevator is an interesting place to observe how people in close spaces avoid interaction.

3.   a. My neighbor's large, formal flower garden looks odd next to his small, modest house.
     b. I'll probably tell my grandchildren about the time I got lost in a museum overnight.

5.   After cleaning up the mess from the picnic, I took the kids home to their various houses all over town, unloaded the van, and _____ went into the house to crawl into bed.

F.   Read the following narrative paragraph and answer the questions that follow.

A customer taught me a lesson one morning when I was working in the designer sportswear area of a large department store at the mall. To begin with, the day started as usual, with straightening the racks of expensive blouses, skirts and slacks. I had been working at the store between school terms and could barely afford to dress for work, much less buy anything in the department where I worked. About 10:15, a very well dressed woman approached my co-worker. Then, a man in a torn shirt, dusty overalls, and work boots came up to me. I was certain he must be in the wrong department. He said, "My wife seen a bright yellow blouse in here that she said she's like to have for her birthday, and I've come to buy it for her. You reckon you could help me find it? She said it don't have no sleeves." I wanted to ask him whether he was in the right store, but I hesitated. The only blouse that fit his description was a $250 shell in the Anne Klein collection, so I reluctantly showed it to him. He smiled and said, "That must be it!" He pulled out a roll of hundred dollar bills and peeled off three to pay me. I was ashamed that I had prejudged him as I gave him change and wrapped the blouse for him to take home.

1.   Underline the topic sentence in the above narrative paragraph.

2.   Circle any transitional word or phrase that is used for coherence.

3.   Using a carat (^) and writing above the line, insert any one transitional word or phrase at a spot where it will improve coherence.

4.   Cross out one sentence that is not in unity.

5.   In your own words, write what you think is the writer's reason (or the point) for writing this narrative.

_____

4. a. My sister's prom experience inspired me to make better plans before I went to my own prom.
   b. There is a difference between punishment and discipline.

5. a. Josh cherishes his old football jersey even though he can no longer wear it.
   b. My first week as a summer camp counselor was not as easy as I had expected it would be.

D. For the next two questions, put the events below the topic sentence in the best order for a narrative. Number from 1 to 5, with the first event in the sequence labeled number 1.

1. Topic sentence: Being responsive to a sudden change in the weather saved the day at my aunt's retirement party.
   _____ An hour before guests were due to arrive, a slow but steady rain began to fall.
   _____ For weeks, the plans for the celebration had called for it to be held outside.
   _____ Then, just as the first guests were greeted indoors, a gust of wind blew the huge tent to the ground, crushing the decorations that were still under it.
   _____ The morning of the party, a large tent was erected on the lawn of my aunt's lake house.
   _____ Chairs and refreshments were quickly moved indoors before anyone arrived.

2. Topic sentence: My grandson's first fishing expedition with his dad was a day they'll both remember fondly.
   _____ Their first stop when they got to the beautiful river was a bait shop where they ran into Luke's best friend Seth and his dad.
   _____ They woke up at 5:00 a.m. that bright June morning, both excited about the trip.
   _____ The four of them told stories, laughed, and even caught fish until late in the evening.
   _____ Luke had been sick for several months, and his dad Ted had promised him that they would go fishing when the doctor said Luke was well enough.
   _____ The evening before the hour-long drive to Current River, they packed Ted's truck with travel chairs, tackle boxes, and a cooler full of food.

E. Supply transitional words that will help make the following samples from narrative writing more coherent.

1. Chad started the job of checking the oil correctly and realized he needed to add a quart. Unfortunately, he _____ reached for transmission fluid instead of motor oil.

2. The doctor's office waiting room was quiet as just one other patient and I waited to be called. _____, a woman came screaming into the room.

3. Giving the dog a bath is Yaxi's least favorite job. _____, she has to capture the reluctant animal before he can escape into the woods behind her house, which he tries to do as soon as he sees the dog tub.

4. It took all afternoon to get my mother's prescriptions the day she came home from the hospital. _____ we got home and she went to bed, I began calling the pharmacies to see who carried the unusual medicine she needed. I ended up going to three different stores.

A. Circle the letter of the choice that best completes the following sentences.

   1. When a writer uses narration to develop a paragraph or essay, he or she is relating _____.
     a. examples to show what a general idea or thing is like
     b. a story that makes a main point
     c. reasons for an opinion, circumstance, or action

   2. The best kind of order to use in presenting the details of a narrative is _____.
     a. chronological, also known as time
     b. order of importance
     c. spatial order

   3. The main point of a narrative paragraph or essay is _____.
     a. the descriptions that help the reader envision the scene and persons present
     b. the reason for relating the incident or event, why it is worth telling
     c. helping the reader understand the difference between categories in a larger group

B. Read each of the following pairs of topics for a paragraph or essay. Which of the two would be more suited to development by narration? Circle the letter of your choice.

   1. a. A terrible haircut
      b. The worst date you ever had

   2. a. The life cycle of a butterfly
      b. The death of my dog Skip when I was nine

   3. a. Passing my lifesaving exam
      b. What an insecure person is like

   4. a. A crime that I witnessed
      b. My grandmother's kitchen

   5. a. The advantages of leasing a car
      b. An exchange between a customer and a street vendor

C. In each of the following, circle the letter of the better narration main idea sentence.

   1. a. Meeting my fiancé's parents for the first time was a nerve-wracking experience.
      b. I met my future mother-in-law last weekend.

   2. a. Once I witnessed a bank robbery in a town I was passing through.
      b. An unplanned incident with my elderly neighbor taught me a lesson in compassion.

   3. a. My father grew up in Merida, Mexico, and my uncle's family is still there.
      b. Something that happened during a visit with my cousin in Mexico helped me to better understand my father.

PART II

Methods of Development/ Rhetorical Modes

2. Athletes who are well known after retirement from sports
   a. Michael Jordan
   b. _____

3. Storybook character costumes that are available to rent for Halloween
   a. Little Red Riding Hood
   b. _____

4. Work benefits that a company can offer
   a. day care center for children of employees
   b. _____

E. **For each phrase below, there is a list. Circle the letter of the item in each list that is NOT an example of the phrase.**

1. Pieces of gym equipment found in most sports clubs
   a. Stationary bikes
   b. Massage tables
   c. Rowing machines
   d. Treadmills

2. Kitchen utensils that most cooks use regularly
   a. Cheese grater
   b. Vegetable peeler
   c. Bread basket
   d. Can opener

3. Adventurous vacation activities
   a. Bicycling alongside a river
   b. Rock climbing
   c. Parasailing over the ocean
   d. Riding a zip line over the jungle

4. Cartoon characters my parents used to watch as kids
   a. Mickey Mouse
   b. Bugs Bunny
   c. Donald Duck
   d. Homer Simpson

F. **Supply transitional words that will help make the following samples from illustration writing more coherent. Use a different transitional word in the two items that follow.**

1. All of my favorite foods can be found in ethnic restaurants. _____, I love the taste of spanikopita, a Greek pastry. _____, any Asian eatery that offers dishes with lemon grass wins my vote.

2. My older brother Roger did things to tease and irritate me just to be mean. _____, he stole my phone, hid it, and called its number to watch me search for it frantically.

G. Read the following illustration paragraph and answer the questions that follow.

    Safe in a dresser drawer in my spare bedroom I keep the clothes I no longer wear, but which carry such sentimental value that I cannot throw them away. For instance, I have an old sweater of my mother's, on which she embroidered the initials of her maiden name when she went away to school for the first time. She went to college a long way away from her family in Ohio. The drawer also holds the letter jacket my dad won in track. When he died, Mom gave it to me because of my own love for running and jumping. Another item is a pair of gloves, far too tiny for my hands even then, given to me by my first real boyfriend. There are several other items in this drawer, but perhaps my favorite is a little dress my grandmother made for me the first time I spent a week at her house. It was a beautiful long pink creation; she even made a matching one for my doll! As badly as I need space, I will always keep these special clothes, reminders of dear people and times.

1. What is the writer providing examples <u>of</u>?

_____

2. What are four main examples provided in this paragraph?

_____ _____

_____ _____

3. Add here one additional supporting detail that could belong in this paragraph.

_____

4. Cross out one sentence that does not belong in this paragraph.

A.   Circle the letter of the choice that best completes the following sentences.

1. Which one of the following is **not** a word that might appear in the main idea sentence of a process paragraph or essay?
    a. how
    b. way
    c. reason

2. Which type of order is most often appropriate for explaining a process?
    a. chronological, or time
    b. spatial, or location
    c. importance, or climax

3. Process analysis is a strategy that writers use to _____.
    a. provide details about what something looks like
    b. give instructions or explain how something works
    c. explain different members of a group

4. Which of the following is not something a writer might include to help a reader understand the process he or she is writing about?
    a. a list of outcomes of different but similar processes
    b. a warning about what might happen if the process isn't followed correctly
    c. a list of materials or skills needed to carry out the process well

B.   Read each of the following pairs of topics for a paragraph or an essay. Which of the two would be more suited to development by process explanation? Circle the letter of your choice.

1. a. the pictures I chose to decorate my office
    b. setting up a home office

2. a. what happens if you do not take care of your teeth
    b. three important things to do to make your home safer

3. a. personality traits of shy people
    b. how my family celebrates birthdays

4. a. the sequence of actions required to open the retail store where I work
    b. my sister-in-law's hometown in Puerto Rico

5. a. benefits of being an only child
    b. steps a parent can take to teach her only child social skills

C. **In each of the following, circle the letter of the better main idea sentence for a process explanation.**

1. a. There is a knack to opening an oyster, but it is not hard to learn.
   b. Ants have been compared to human beings because of their social structures.

2. a. I will never forget the mild summer evening when I first met my present boyfriend.
   b. If you want to catch the eye of a person you'd like to date, here are three simple strategies to try.

3. a. Jerry could not believe the terrible condition of the road we were on.
   b. The company I work for has reduced energy consumption by following several new policies.

4. a. Installing new software on your computer is a fairly simple procedure.
   b. An optimist is a person who sees the positive side of situations.

5. a. Some talk-show hosts are more outrageous than their unusual guests.
   b. Getting a room painted involves a series of tasks, from planning to clean up.

D. **For the next two questions, put the events below the topic sentence in the best order for a process explanation. Number from 1 to 5, with the first event in the sequence being number 1.**

1. <u>Topic sentence:</u> A successful vegetable garden begins with steps you take to prepare your plot.
   ____ Remove the grass turf from the top of this chosen spot, and pull out weeds.
   ____ Now your garden plot is prepared for planting.
   ____ You'll first have to choose an area of your yard that gets good sunlight and drains well.
   ____ Once the grass and weeds are removed, use a garden rake to comb the roots and rocks out.
   ____ The last step of preparation is to feed your soil the nutrients it needs by fertilizing.

2. <u>Topic sentence:</u> Applying "straight" make-up for the stage, for a character who doesn't need to be aged, is a process that most actors have mastered.
   ____ Then the actor applies lipstick, using a color that is slightly darker than natural.
   ____ An actor starts with a clean face, all formerly applied make-up removed.
   ____ The first thing an actor applies is the base, often called "pancake," which gives overall color.
   ____ The experienced actor will finish with some loose powder to ensure that the lights won't reflect on a shiny nose.
   ____ Most think it best to work secondly on the eyes, using color on the lid, eyeliner, and mascara.

E. Supply transitional words that will help make the following samples from a process explanation more coherent.

1. My mother and father have the same routine every morning. _____, Dad goes to get the paper while Mother makes coffee.

2. _____ putting the clothes in the washer, you should choose the water level and temperature that are most appropriate for your load of clothes.

3. In the event of an electrical blackout during a storm, first find the flashlight. _____, go around your home and turn off all unnecessary appliances.

F. Read the following process paragraph and answer the questions that follow.

(1) If you want to take care of your teeth, there are a few dental hygiene habits you must develop, and all they require is a bit of time on a regular basis. (2) The most frequent thing you must do is brush your teeth. (3) Do this twice a day for at least two minutes each time. (4) Hold the toothbrush at a 45-degree angle to your teeth, and make sure the bristles penetrate gently into the gum line. (5) Use a soft brush and brush gently. (6) Floss your teeth daily. (7) You need to guide the floss between every two teeth and clean the area between your teeth and gums. (8) This is done to remove plaque. (9) Finally, you must have your teeth cleaned professionally at least twice a year. (10) This cleaning helps prevent tooth decay and gum disease. (11) People who suffer from diabetes are more likely to develop gum disease. (12) Having healthy teeth into your later years is well worth the time you put into these good habits.

1. What is the process this paragraph presents?

2. What are the benefits of knowing and doing this process?

3. Sentences numbered 3, 4, 5, and 6 are all the same kind of sentences, a type used more often in process analysis than in any other type of college writing. What kind of sentence are these? (hint: What is the subject of each of these?)

4. Why did the writer include sentence 8? (What is its reason for being in the paragraph?)

5. What is the number of a sentence that does not belong in this paragraph?

6. Which of the following best describes the order of supporting details used in this paragraph?
   a. time order
   b. most frequent to least frequent
   c. most crucial to least crucial

A. Circle T for true or F for false for each of the following statements.

T F 1. There is more than one type of process writing: giving instructions directly to the reader or explaining how something works or worked.

T F 2. In a process essay, each specific explanation about a step in a process must have its own separate paragraph.

T F 3. Time order is the only correct way to achieve coherence when explaining how some process in business or society can work.

T F 4. The topic sentence or thesis statement for a process explanation should make clear the intended outcome, or what will result from following the steps.

T F 5. The writer of a process should be consistent in point of view, using pronouns carefully throughout the writing.

B. Read each of the following pairs of topics for a paragraph or an essay. Which of the two is more suited to development by process explanation? Circle the letter of your choice.

1. a. registering for next term's classes
   b. the advantages of working at home

2. a. a creative person you know
   b. using the office copier correctly

3. a. card games children can enjoy on a rainy day
   b. how a child can make his or her own board game

4. a. the life cycle of a gypsy moth
   b. your ideal wilderness vacation trip

5. a. ways to save energy costs at home
   b. why you changed jobs

C. In each of the following, circle the letter of the better main idea sentence for a process explanation.

1. a. Many over-the-counter drugs used to be available only by prescription.
   b. Coloring my own hair is an easy job that saves me money.

2. a. The system I devised for storing and restocking my art supplies works well for me.
   b. An observer would never believe that Eduardo and Felipe are actually twin brothers.

3. a. The music education program at my son's elementary school should not be ended.
   b. Helping a child develop a love of books is not a difficult task if a parent starts early.

4. a. Shopping for a used car can result in success if you follow a few steps.
   b. *Mad* magazine, with its satirical cartoons, has been popular with teenagers for decades.

5. a. New sports drinks, such as "smart" water have appeared on the market.
   b. Anyone can make a proper cup of tea by following this time-tested procedure.

D. For the next two questions, put the events below the topic sentence in the best order for a process explanation. Number from 1 to 5, with the first event in the sequence being number 1.

1. Topic sentence: After taking several deliberate steps to evaluate my first choice of career, I decided to change my major.

   _____ I also enrolled in an introductory class in planning children's recreational learning activities.

   _____ Eventually, my experiences with these two trial steps led me to realize that I would be happier in a quieter setting, so I changed my major to accounting.

   _____ My first check-up step was volunteering at my church's daycare center, where I found the environment stressful for a shy person like myself.

   _____ I originally declared childhood education as a major based on my mom's love of teaching, but I began to have doubts when I realized how tired she always is.

   _____ This class showed me that I lack the personality to lead effective learning play.

2. Topic sentence: A friend's grandfather taught me this easy way to prepare a good, old-fashioned hot dog.

   _____ While they are cooking, cut up the special ingredient, sweet Vidalia onions.

   _____ Put the franks in lightly salted water that is already boiling, and cook them for ten minutes.

   _____ A good hot dog begins with the proper basics: fresh buns and all-beef franks.

   _____ Layer a generous helping of canned chili on top and serve hot!

   _____ Line the bun with your favorite variety of mustard, and then put the chopped onions in under the hot dog.

E. Supply transitional words that will help make the following samples from a process explanation more coherent.

1. Saving money at the grocery store starts at home. _____, get a pencil and paper, and take a look in your refrigerator and pantry to see what you need.

2. _____ taking the cake out of the oven, insert a toothpick in the middle, and see if it comes out dry. This test will tell you whether the cake is done.

3. Push the number of the floor where you want to stop. Step back to allow other passengers to have room to enter. _____, stand quietly, waiting, and do not make eye contact.

F. Read the following process paragraph and answer the questions that follow.

(1) Making your own pizza at home is easy, economical, and enjoyable. (2) Start with gathering the essential ingredients. (3) You will need some roll-out dough (available at your grocery store near rolled-up cookie dough), your favorite brand of sauce, and cheese. (4) A bag of shredded cheese, with cheddar and mozzarella, works well. (5) Choose about four or five topping ingredients, such as pepperoni, onions, or mushrooms. (6) Be creative; think about including pineapple or raisins for a different taste. (7) One time, a friend and I made a pizza with peanuts on it! (8) Once you have your ingredients assembled, preheat the oven to about 400 degrees. (9) If you don't do this, you'll be waiting a long time after the pizza is put together before you can bake it. (10) Roll out the dough on a baking sheet. (11) Pour the sauce evenly over the surface of the dough. (12) Add your toppings, meats first and then vegetables. (13) Sprinkle cheese on top, and pop your creation into the hot oven. (14) In about twenty minutes, you will be enjoying a hot homemade pizza.

1. What process does this paragraph present?

2. What are the benefits of knowing and doing this process?

3. What is the number of the sentence that does not belong in this paragraph?

4. Add your own transitional words to improve the coherence in this paragraph. Use a caret (^) and write the word or phrase clearly above the line.

5. Which of the following best describes the order of supporting details used in this paragraph? Circle your answer.
   a. time order
   b. most crucial to least crucial
   c. space order

A. **Circle the letter of the choice that best completes the following sentences.**

1. The purpose of a definition paragraph or essay is to
    a. convince the reader to change his opinion about a term
    b. narrate how the meaning of a term was learned
    c. explain what a term means
    d. divide a general term into its possible categories

2. A definition paragraph or essay goes beyond the dictionary definition because it
    a. develops ideas about what a term might mean to various people
    b. tells what the term means to the writer in particular
    c. gives the part of speech of the term
    d. uses slang and community dialects to explain a term

3. A technique that would NOT be used by a writer to develop a definition is to
    a. provide a synonym for the term
    b. tell what the meaning is not (use contrast)
    c. give an example of the term
    d. present several other terms that have similar meanings

4. Which of the following is NOT a reason a writer might have to write a definition?
    a. the term is a specific word that is very rarely used in written language
    b. the term is a technical one, with specific meaning
    c. the term is unknown to the writer's audience
    d. the term may mean different things to different people, and the writer intends to indicate what it means to him or her

B. **Read each of the following pairs of topics for a paragraph or an essay. Which of the two would be more suited to development by definition? Circle the letter of your choice.**

1. a. a stapler
    b. road rage

2. a. responsibility
    b. making an omelet

3. a. Kwanzaa
    b. a Key West sunset

4. a. charisma
    b. brain

C. **In each of the following, circle the letter of the better definition main idea sentence.**

1. a. The duel between Alexander Hamilton and Aaron Burr is a famous one.
    b. A pack rat is a person who can't stand to throw anything away.

2. a. Nostalgia is the feeling of looking back on the past with tender fondness.
   b. Geography is my niece's favorite subject in her middle school studies.

3. a. Osteoporosis is a physical condition characterized by decreasing bone mass.
   b. Semolina is a cereal in England that I really do not care for.

4. a. A hero is capable of things that no one else can do and is heroic in the process.
   b. In a legal context, a finding is discovery of information that results from an investigation or a judge's examination.

D. **In each of the following formal definition sentences, underline once the group or category that the term belongs to, and underline twice the part that tells how the term is different from other words in that group or category.**

1. Depression is a mental condition marked by extreme sadness, inactivity, poor

   concentration, and hopelessness.

2. An optimist is a person who consistently looks for the positive aspects of a situation.

3. An expatriate is a person who has withdrawn from allegiance to and residence in his or

   her native country.

4. Martial law is a system of governing based on the military authority of an occupying

   power.

E. **For each of the following words, decide whether a writer's purpose in defining would be to provide technical information or a personal definition sharing his or her own view about what the word means. Write <u>tech</u> for technical or <u>pers</u> for personal.**

1. relaxation _____

2. fairness _____

3. odometer _____

4. jurisdiction _____

F. Read the following definition paragraph and answer the questions that follow.

(1) Persistence is the action of going toward a goal despite opposition or possible risk of failure. (2) It is the quality that allows a person to stick to a plan when the process is difficult. (3) The word "persistence" comes from the verb "to persist" which comes from a Latin word that means "to take a stand." (4) I would call my great-aunt, Reba McCoy, a persistent person. (5) A persistent person doesn't give up or complain; he or she keeps on keeping on, however small the steps toward fulfillment of the goal. (6) Sometimes small steps are all that a person can make. (7) A good example of persistence is the graduation from college of a student whose educational journey requires six or seven years to complete. (8) Another example of persistence, also known as perseverance, is the continuation of a rigorous diet and exercise program by a person who is determined to lose weight and improve fitness. (9) When a person persists, he or she resolves to continue doing what must be done to succeed at a goal. (10) It's a quality that can take a person a long way toward accomplishing any meaningful goal.

1. Underline the formal definition in the above paragraph.

2. In which sentence does the writer use the technique of contrast to define the term?

3. In which sentence does the writer give information about word origin to define?

4. What is one example from the paragraph of a person with persistence?

5. Which sentence does nothing to help develop the definition?

A. Circle T for true or F for false for each of the following statements.

T F 1. The topic sentence for a definition paragraph or essay often comes straight out of a dictionary.

T F 2. A formal definition is the only appropriate way to begin a definition paragraph.

T F 3. A definition must be developed with supporting explanation, which can come in several ways, such as example or synonym.

T F 4. A circular definition, which only repeats a form of the term being defined and adds nothing, is not useful.

B. Read each of the following pairs of topics for a paragraph or an essay. Which of the two would be more suited to development by definition? Circle the letter of your choice.

1. a. my first kiss
    b. prejudice

2. a. conservation
    b. animal

3. a. quitting smoking
    b. myth

4. a. utopia
    b. rainy Saturday in November

C. In each of the following, circle the letter of the better definition main idea sentence.

1. a. Jargon is language used in a specialized field by people who know the meanings of the terminology.
    b. Truth sometimes can be stranger than fiction.

2. a. Living with another person in a one-bedroom apartment can strain a friendship.
    b. Insomnia is the physical problem of prolonged inability to sleep.

3. a. Monogamy is the practice of remaining monogamous.
    b. The altar is a table or stand in the sacred part of a place of worship used for devotional observances.

4. a. A unicorn is a legendary beast that looks like a horse with a single, spiral horn.
    b. Solitude is the condition of being solitary or, in other words, solo.

D. In each of the following formal definition sentences, underline once the group or category that the term belongs to, and underline twice the part that tells how the term is different from other words in that group or category.

1. Paella is a Spanish food consisting of seasoned rice and some kind of spicy meat.

2. A loner is a person who prefers his or her own company over that of others and who values independence.

3. A defibrillator is an electronic device used in medicine to overcome the effect of tremors in the muscles of the heart.

4. A manatee is a sea mammal that lives in warm coastal waters and has two flippers and a large oval tail.

E. There are several ways to develop a definition. Match each of the following sentences from a definition paragraph with the method used to define the term.

   a. defines by giving an example
   b. defines by contrast, saying what the term is not
   c. defines by providing a synonym
   d. defines by giving information about the origin of the word

1. _____ Used in measuring, the word notch is a unit of comparison, like a degree, grade, or step.

2. _____ Forgiving is wiping the slate clean, letting someone off the hook. If you tell a friend not to worry any more about the way she hurt your feelings, then you have forgiven her.

3. _____ The meaning of the word "flavor" goes back to the Latin term for "to emit odor."

4. _____ The kind of headhunting done in business today does not involve savages with knives looking for a sign of victory.

F. Read the following definition paragraph and answer the questions that follow.

(1) Being a good citizen does not mean merely voting in an election every two or four years. (2) A citizen is a person who is actively involved in community affairs on an ongoing basis. (3) It is someone who invests in service to a community or nation in exchange for rights and privileges. (4) For instance, a good citizen might wish to volunteer at a local public school where he or she tutors a student in reading or works in the office. (5) Many successful businesspeople give up time to help others in many ways. (6) Being a citizen requires an awareness that a person belongs to a place as an essential member, whose talents are needed for the good of all. (7) Even the original meaning of the word is related to the French for "city." (8) Good citizens take the term seriously enough to give something back to the city or community they belong to.

1. Underline the formal definition in the above paragraph.

2. In which sentence does the writer use the technique of contrast to define the term?

3. In which sentence does the writer give information about word origin?

4. What is one example of citizenship from the paragraph?

5. Which sentence does nothing to develop the definition?

A. Circle the letter of the choice that best completes the following sentences.

1. Classification is writing that
   a. organizes according to more important reasons and less important reasons
   b. organizes by how alike or different two things are
   c. organizes a large group into categories according to a quality or characteristic

2. Which of the following is <u>not</u> an example of a basis for classification, also known as classifying principle?
   a. size
   b. advantages and disadvantages
   c. cost

3. Which of the following is <u>not</u> something a writer must be careful about in establishing the subgroups, or categories?
   a. making sure that the groups are exactly the same size
   b. making sure that the groups do not overlap, or have characteristics in common
   c. making sure that there is a point, or overall reason, for telling about the categories

B. Read each of the following pairs of topics for a paragraph or essay. Which of the two would be more suited to development by classification? Circle the letter of your choice.

1. a. my bakery job
   b. desserts

2. a. horse breeds
   b. equipment for grooming a horse

3. a. foods
   b. my favorite meal

4. a. why I enjoy being outdoors
   b. outdoor activities

C. In each of the following, circle the letter of the better main idea sentence to develop by classification.

1. a. Midway Community College offers several kinds of courses that will help me prepare for my career.
   b. There are two ways to find out if you and the person you're dating are truly compatible.

2. a. Dad uses different bait according to whether he is bottom-fishing or fly-fishing.
   b. The books-on-tape section of my favorite used bookstore has selections in four categories.

3. a. My girlfriend and I especially enjoy cooking three types of ethnic foods.
   b. Children's playgrounds can be full of dangers.

4. a. People stay away from voting places for reasons that tend to fall into one of several categories.
   b. My friend Hamid is really suited to being a salesperson because of his outgoing personality.

D. **Each of the following test items has a large group written in bold caps. Under it are two subgroups. In the blank, write the name of a third subgroup that fits the classifying principle. Be sure this third group will not overlap with the first two.**

1. **SEVERE WEATHER**
   hurricanes
   thunderstorm

   _____

2. **SPORTS**
   games you play on an indoor court
   games you play in the water

   _____

3. **MAIL**
   personal letters
   junk mail

   _____

E. **In the next three items, there is a large group written in bold caps followed by four subgroups. One of these subgroups does not fit under the heading because it _overlaps_ at least one other subgroup. Cross out the subgroup that overlaps at least one other group.**

1. **THINGS FOUND IN AN ATTIC**
   Christmas decorations
   old furniture
   things that belonged to my grandmother
   unused clothes

2. **TYPES OF VACATIONS**
   trip to enjoy nature
   trip to take with close friends
   trip to sample special foods
   trip to experience art and theater

3. **PEOPLE ENJOYING THE BEACH**
   teenagers
   swimmers
   surfers
   sunbathers

F. **Supply transitional words that will help make the following samples from classification writing more coherent.**

1. One group of readers goes to a book for escape, while _____ group goes to the bookshelf to learn something.

2. Trees can be categorized according to the gifts they provide. Some provide food, others provide shade and protection, _____ still others provide beauty.

3. One category of shopper looks for only what is absolutely necessary. A _____ type is ready to buy anything as long as it's on sale.

G. **Read the following classification paragraph and answer the questions that follow.**

(1) Visitors to the New River Festival attended for a variety of reasons, but each person tended to fall into one of three categories. (2) One group of folks was there to shop. (3) The festival was filled with booths full of all kinds of wares, from homemade jams to birdhouses that looked like Noah's ark to fine art in fancy frames. (4) My sister-in-law spent all day shopping and chatting with the vendors. (5) She bought a nice oil lamp made out of a rock. (6) Another group of festival-goers was there to listen to the music. (7) The small stage, set up beside the river, featured different bands all day, mostly bluegrass and gospel. (8) Some listeners never moved from their chairs while one band after another entertained them. (9) Dad was parked in front of the stage from midmorning until sunset. (10) The last group of people was not interested in any special feature the festival had to offer, but was there just to walk around and talk to neighbors they don't see often. (11) My mom's cousin, who lives in the area, was one of those. (12) I enjoyed observing the different people with their various reasons for being outdoors on a beautiful fall day along a mountain river.

1. What is the classifying principle this writer used?

2. List any two transitional words that help make the paragraph coherent:

_____   _____

3. If the writer wanted to add this sentence, where would it fit?

   These locals wanted to catch up on the news and swap gossip.

   It belongs between the sentences now numbered _____ and _____.

4. Which sentence is not in unity and should be removed? _____

5. Which family member is provided as an example of the second group? _____

A.   **Circle T for true or F for false for each of the following statements.**

   T F   1. Subgroups, or categories, in a classification must be established according to a basis or classifying principle.

   T F   2. A classification paper may discuss a large group divided into two types.

   T F   3. In addition to having a basis for dividing the large group, the writer must also have a unifying reason for the classification.

   T F   4. It is acceptable for the categories, or subgroups, in a classification to overlap with each other.

B.   **Read each of the following pairs of topics for a paragraph or an essay. Which of the two would be more suited to development by classification? Circle the letter of your choice.**

   1.   a. people at the beach
        b. a beautiful beach sunset

   2.   a. tangerines
        b. fruit

   3.   a. your favorite department store
        b. shoppers

   4.   a. visitors from out of town
        b. your household rules for visitors

C.   **In each of the following, circle the letter of the better main idea sentence to develop by classification.**

   1.   a. Helena, my former roommate from Finland, enjoys all kinds of American music.
        b. The candy aisle at the grocery store is full of goodies that can be divided into several distinct groups.

   2.   a. Jeans manufacturers market their styles to three different audiences, each of which buys jeans for a certain reason.
        b. I know of two ways to fade jeans by using different laundry products.

   3.   a. Some music videos are violent, some contain only a small amount of violence, and others have no violence at all.
        b. Each person I observed at the doctor's office was doing something different to fill time waiting.

4. a. Small children repeat some surprising words or phrases that they have overheard from adults.

   b. The jewelry in my case can be divided into separate groups: funky, functional, and fancy.

D. **Each of the following items has a large group written in bold caps. Under it, there are two subgroups. In the blank, write the name of a third subgroup that fits the classifying principle. Be sure this third group will not overlap with the first two.**

1. **TV SHOWS**
    reality shows
    situation comedies

    _____

2. **DESSERTS**
    made of chocolate
    made of custard

    _____

3. **PARTIES**
    holiday
    special milestones (graduation, retirement)

    _____

E. **In the next three items, there is a large group written in bold caps followed by four subgroups. One of these subgroups does not fit under the heading because it _overlaps_ at least one other subgroup. Cross out the subgroup that overlaps at least one other group.**

1. **WINDOW TREATMENTS**
    blinds
    coverings
    curtains
    shades

2. **RESTAURANTS**
    Asian specialties
    Mexican specialties
    Mediterannean specialties
    dessert specialties

3. **THINGS FOUND IN THE GARAGE**
    yard maintenance equipment
    lawnmower
    car maintenance equipment
    unused household appliances

F. **Supply transitional words that will help make the following samples from classification writing more coherent.**

1. A typical medicine cabinet in a household where children live contains several types of substances. _____ is topical ointments to use on skin problems.

2. The pictures covering my grandma's mantel and piano top have three kinds of frames: wood, silver, and china. The first kind, wood, mostly holds pictures of houses my family members have called home. The _____ kind, silver, is for photos of special occasions.

G. **Read the following classification paragraph and answer the questions that follow.**

(1) My movie club, which is made up of three women friends and myself, especially enjoys three types of movies. (2) We enjoy getting together to rent movies with a romantic plot line, those based on true stories of people overcoming hardships, and those that present stories of strong, independent women. (3) The first type of movie we like is the kind that usually stars fairly famous actors and ends with the girl and boy together, living happily ever after. (4) Romantic movies leave us feeling light-hearted. (5) *Serendipity* was such a movie. (6) The second type often reminds us of how hard the world can be but leaves us with a feeling of empowerment. (7) An example of this kind of movie is *Hurricane*. (8) My friend Sara saw that one three times. (9) The third kind we like to experience together inspires us to use strong women as role models. (10) When we leave this kind of movie, we usually talk over dinner about the characteristics we admire. (11) Our movie club has settled on these three types of plot lines as our favorites.

1. What is the classifying principle used in this paragraph?

2. What does this paragraph need in order to balance the development of the categories?

3. Which sentence is not in unity and should be removed?

4. If the writer revised the topic sentence to include a fourth category, what is a type of movie that would fit with this classifying principle?

   Movies about _____

5. Circle two words in the above paragraph that show the reader that it is a classification.

A. Circle the letter of the choice that best completes the following sentences.

1. Comparing and contrasting is writing that presents
    a. similar reasons for two events or phenomena
    b. similarities and differences between two ideas, objects, people, or places
    c. descriptions of two or more ideas, objects, people, or places

2. The purpose of a comparison/contrast paragraph or essay is to
    a. tell how the two things are alike and how they are different
    b. list qualities of two objects or people
    c. explain similarities and differences in order to make a point or draw a conclusion

3. Which of the following is the best guideline for choosing the topics for an effective comparison and/or contrast paper?
    a. choose two things that fall into the same general category and have some similarities and some differences
    b. choose two things that are exactly alike in every way but one
    c. choose two things that are completely different except for one common quality

4. Comparison/Contrast paragraphs or essays can be organized using either of two possible patterns. Which of the following is <u>not</u> a way to organize such a paper?
    a. *block method*; writer tells all the details about one topic, then all about the other
    b. *alternating* or *point-by-point method*; writer tells about one quality at a time
    c. mixing the similarities and differences in order of importance to the writer

B. Read each of the following pairs of topics for a paragraph or an essay. Which of the two would be more suited to development by the comparison and contrast method? Circle your choice.

1. a. a job at McDonald's and a job at Wendy's
    b. a job at McDonald's and a job at NAPA Auto Parts Store

2. a. two good friends of yours, Nate and Luke
    b. a baseball fan and a Scrabble expert

3. a. your favorite restaurant and your parents' favorite restaurant
    b. a bowling alley and a used car lot

4. a. the way your cat acts today and the way she acted yesterday
    b. your cat and your neighbor's cat

C. **In each of the following, circle the letter of the better main idea sentence to develop by comparison and contrast.**

1. a. Sherbet and sorbet are two delicious cold desserts that differ in content, taste, and nutritional value.
   b. Several new immigration laws are affecting the waiting period for people hoping for a work visa in America.

2. a. Both of the high schools in my town offer the same extracurricular sports and clubs.
   b. The atmosphere at Clark Community College is more welcoming than the one at nearby Blake River Community College.

3. a. My brother and I found two suitable nursing homes in our town for our ailing mother, but we were impressed by three differences in their policies.
   b. There are several signs that a beloved older relative may be ready to move into an assisted living environment.

4. a. Two methods of gardening, the traditional one and a new concept called "permaculture," result in beautiful gardens but require differing amounts of work.
   b. I attend worship services at two churches, depending on my mood.

D. **Imagine that you are prewriting for a comparison/contrast paragraph about two different houses you have lived in. Use your imagination, and fill in the blanks below with possible supporting details.**

1. Two ways the two houses are alike:
   a. Both of the houses _____
   b. They both _____

2. Two ways the two houses are different:
   a. One house has _____ but the other one has
      _____.
   b. The _____ in the first house is _____,
      and in the second house it is _____.

E. **Supply transitional words that will help make the following examples from comparison/contrast writing more coherent.**

1. _____ Aunt Rose and Aunt Ida are great cooks, _____ they concentrate their skills on different types of dishes: Rose specializes in Norwegian food and Ida in Italian.

2. Rolf is a dedicated father. His brother, Fred, _____, never even visits his children.

F. **The next two items will check your understanding of methods of organizing a comparison/contrast paragraph or essay.**

1. Below left, there is a rough outline for a comparison/contrast paper about two neighborhoods. It follows what is often called the "block" pattern. Take the same information and reorganize to fit another pattern or method of organization. Fill in the outline on the right with words or phrases from the version from the left.

      Neighborhood 1   _____
        Size of lots   _____
        Types of homes   _____
        Closeness to city   _____

      Neighborhood 2   _____
        Size of lots   _____
        Types of homes   _____
        Closeness to city   _____

2. Below left, there is a rough outline for a comparison/contrast paper about two car models. It follows what is often called an "alternating" pattern. Take the same information and reorganize to fit another pattern or method of organization. Fill in the outline on the right with the words or phrases from the version on the left.

      Gas mileage   _____
        Car 1   _____
        Car 2   _____

      Horsepower   _____
        Car 1   _____
        Car 2   _____

      Warranty offered   _____
        Car 1   _____
        Car 2   _____

G. **Read the following comparison/contrast paragraph and answer the questions that follow.**

Each winter, when my family plans the next summer's trip to the beach, we hold a family meeting to discuss the options. Our two possibilities this year, Myrtle Beach and Edisto Island, are both beautiful seaside vacation spots, but they differ in several ways. Myrtle Beach is a popular resort area that offers many different activities for those of us with varied interests. Mom can go shopping, the younger kids can enjoy the rides or play arcade games, Dad can play golf, and I can go parasailing. Nightlife at Myrtle Beach is also full of possibilities: restaurants, concerts, theater, and nightclubs. Myrtle Beach is crowded and full of visitors though, and we will probably have to search for a spot on the sand to lay a beach towel. Edisto Island, with its unusual name, is a place my uncle's family went last year. It has much less development and fewer activities to offer than Myrtle Beach. There are only a few art shops in the area, no arcades, and the closest golf course is miles away. It appeals to nature lovers who just want to collect shells, watch birds, and soak up sun. Nightlife is more of the same, quiet and natural. Thinking about these differences will help my family make a decision about where to go for vacation.

1. What two things are being compared and contrasted?

2. What do these two things have in common?

3. Explain how the writer chose to organize this paragraph.

4. Cross out, in the paragraph above, one sentence that does not belong because it disrupts the organizational pattern.

5. The writer needs to add one sentence in order to improve the coherence of this paragraph. What should that sentence be about?

COMPARISON AND CONTRAST   Test B

A. **Circle T for true or F for false for each of the following statements.**

T F 1. Comparison involves explaining similarities or common features between two things.

T F 2. A writer must never try to explain both similarities and differences in one essay.

T F 3. When contrasting, it is important to choose two items or people who have something in common to begin with.

T F 4. There is only one way to organize a comparison/contrast paragraph or essay.

B. **Read each of the following pairs of topics for a paragraph or an essay. Which of the two would be more suited to development by the comparison and contrast method? Circle the letter of your choice.**

1. a. your first date with your girlfriend and your second date with her
    b. why you changed girlfriends and why you wish you hadn't

2. a. camping at the beach in a tent and staying at a hotel on a trip to Europe
    b. camping at the beach in a tent and camping at the beach in an RV

3. a. two teachers you have had
    b. a teacher you had for psychology and a teacher your sister had for math

4. a. a TV show about family life in the 70s and a TV show about family life today
    b. the uniform of a Civil War soldier and the uniform of an astronaut of 2025

C. **In each of the following, circle the letter of the better main idea sentence to develop by comparison and contrast.**

1. a. My duties at the cotton mill were similar when I worked first shift and third shift, but the working conditions were quite different.
    b. I liked almost everything about working third shift at the mill, except for the hours.

2. a. There are several kinds of materials a painter can use to create a beautiful landscape.
    b. My two closest friends share a love of painting, but their studios are different.

3. a. Although colds and seasonal allergies are both annoying, their symptoms and causes differ.
    b. There are several preventive measures that may help ward off a cold or flu.

4. a. I adopted two dogs from the shelter, instead of just one, for several reasons.
    b. My two cocker spaniels are similar in appearance, but each has her own personality.

D. **Imagine that you are prewriting for a comparison/contrast paragraph about two different parks you have taken children to. Use your imagination, and fill in the blanks below with possible supporting details.**

   1. Two ways the two parks are alike:
     a. Both of the parks are _____
     b. They both _____

   2. Two ways the two parks are different:
     a. One park has _____ and the other one has

      _____.

     b. The _____ at the first park is _____,
      and at the second park it is _____.

E. **Supply transitional words that will help make the following examples from comparison/contrast writing more coherent.**

   1. Keisha's study area is neat and orderly. Her friend Grace, _____, makes a mess studying.

   2. Neither a microwave nor a toaster oven takes up much kitchen space. _____, either one can be mounted under the top shelf to free up space.

F. **The next two items will check your understanding of methods of organizing a comparison/contrast paragraph or essay.**

   1. Below left, there is a rough outline for a comparison/contrast paper about two candidates for city council. It follows what is often called the "block" pattern. Take the same information and reorganize to fit another pattern or method of organization. Fill in the outline on the right with phrases from the version on the left.

     Candidate 1   _____
       Political experience   _____
       Community involvement   _____
       Educational background   _____

     Candidate 2   _____
       Political experience   _____
       Community involvement   _____
       Educational background   _____

2. Below left, there is a rough outline for a comparison/contrast paper about two teachers. It follows what is often called an "alternating" pattern. Take the same information and reorganize to fit another pattern or method of organization. Fill in the outline on the right with the words or phrases from the version on the left.

Knowledge of content material   _____
     Teacher 1   _____
     Teacher 2   _____

Teaching methods   _____
     Teacher 1   _____
     Teacher 2   _____

Amount of work required   _____
     Teacher 1   _____
     Teacher 2   _____

G. Read the following comparison/contrast paragraph and answer the questions that follow.

From their personalities and overall appearances, you would never guess that my younger sisters, Tamara and Kelly, are sisters, much less twins. Tamara is the quiet, shy one who prefers reading in the corner of the den to doing anything else. Her hobby is collecting books signed by their authors. Kelly is a loud, outgoing teenager who enjoys playing sports and riding around with her girlfriends. Tamara never speaks up about an issue without careful consideration, and her comments reflect a lot of thought. Since they are fraternal rather than identical twins, they inherited different genes, quite different, in fact. Tamara is 5'7" tall, with straight, blond hair, and glasses. Kelly is 5'4" tall, her hair is dark and curly, and her eyes are bright blue. Tamara actually has bright blue eyes too, like my other sister and me. The one thing that Tamara and Kelly have in common is a love of family; each enjoys outings and gatherings with the rest of us. We celebrate their birthday with two separate cakes, for our two youngest family members, each different and precious in her own way.

1. What two things or persons are being compared and contrasted?

2. What do these two sisters have in common?

3. Explain how the writer chose to organize this paragraph.

4. Cross out, in the paragraph above, one sentence that does not belong because it disrupts the organizational pattern.

5. The writer needs to add one sentence in order to improve the coherence and development of this paragraph. What should that sentence be about?

A. Circle T for true or F for false for each of the following sentences.

   T F 1. A complex problem usually has only one real cause that is worth explaining.

   T F 2. The writer of a cause and effect paper must be careful not to confuse causes with effects.

B. Read each of the following pairs of topics for a paragraph or an essay. Which of the two would be a more effective topic to develop by cause and effect? Circle the letter of your choice.

   1. a. how my poor eating habits affected my stamina in tennis
       b. reasons to eat right

   2. a. problems with my brother Hal's work habits
       b. why my brother Hal was fired from his last job

   3. a. television shows that kids should not watch
       b. why I chose the gym I belong to

   4. a. how getting a parking ticket led me to my goal to become a lawyer
       b. schools should have tighter security

   5. a. effects of offering a flexible working schedule on my company's business
       b. how people in the American workforce react to stress

C. In each of the following, circle the letter of the main idea sentence that would be more effective in a cause and effect paragraph or essay. Do not choose a sentence if it is not logical, if it is too broad, or if it does not lend itself to development by the cause and effect method.

   1. a. My car broke down because I had bought it from my brother-in-law.
       b. For three reasons, I will never make a major purchase from a family member ever again.

   2. a. On the surface, my marriage ended because of one really bad decision, but two additional underlying problems contributed to the divorce.
       b. Marriages in this country fail for a vast number of reasons.

   3. a. My discomfort with nursing homes can be traced to several bad experiences during visits with my grandmother.
       b. My fear of nursing homes makes me a bad grandson since I refuse to visit my grandmother.

   4. a. Reducing your work hours will lead to getting all A's and to a larger savings account due to more effective management of your money.
       b. For three reasons, reducing my work hours worked out well for me.

D. In each blank in the following sentences, write a transitional word that will help make the combination of ideas coherent.

1. The winter storm laid layers of ice on the tree branches; _____ , many of them broke under the added weight.

2. During her son's illness, Helen missed her most difficult class for a week. She decided, _____ , to drop the course rather than fail it.

E. Use your imagination to do the following sample of prewriting for a cause and effect paper. In the blanks to the left, list three possible causes for the topic in the center, and in the blanks to the right, list three possible effects.

1.

    Causes   Effects

_____

_____   CHANGING JOBS   _____

_____

_____

2.

    Causes   Effects

_____

_____   MOVING TO A NEW   _____
                                        APARTMENT

_____   _____

F. Number each of the following support point sentences to show which sentence should be placed first (1), second, (2) and so on.

Mary Jo began to look for a new job when dissatisfaction overcame the good pay she was earning.

_____ More bothersome, though, was the terrible smell in the work area since the developing chemicals had been changed.

_____ Her first two years in the photo lab had been fine, but then her work conditions began to change.

_____ Equally annoying, a new coworker was so lazy that Mary Jo had to work harder.

_____ Finally, when the boss expected Mary Jo to give up classes to work first shift, she knew her career with the lab was at an end.

_____ For one thing, the relocation of the drive-in window meant that she had to stare into the sun for hours at a time.

G. **In the appropriate spaces below each of the following thesis statements, write the cause and the effect contained in the sentence.**

1. The weather forecast called for snow, so our family changed our plans to hike to Bear Mountain.

    cause _____

    effect _____

2. As more people shop online, malls are less crowded during the holiday season.

    cause _____

    effect _____

H. **Read the following paragraph and answer the questions.**

   When I was only twelve, just starting middle school, my family moved from a rural area to a medium sized city. Going into a much larger school had several unexpected consequences. One change was that there were many other students trying out for the basketball team, so I experienced for the first time the challenge of competing for a place on the team. In my old school, anyone who wanted to play usually could. I had been the leading free throw shooter on my former team. Another change, one that affected my daily routine, was the way lunch worked at the new school. I had to get used to eating lunch at 10:45 in the morning because lunch times were staggered in the small cafeteria. The biggest impact on me, though, was the size of my potential social circle. There were eight seventh grade classes; therefore, I only got to know students in my room and in the room next door. It was odd to see so many kids my own age that I did not know. Since I am an adaptable person, I eventually adjusted to my new school without too much difficulty.

1. Underline the topic sentence of the paragraph.

2. Circle the word in the topic sentence that indicates which will be presented in the paragraph, causes or effects.

3. Cross out the one sentence that is not in unity with the rest of the paragraph.

4. Which of the following describes the order used to achieve coherence?
    a. order of importance
    b. time order

5. Circle three transitional words that help with coherence in the paragraph.

A. Circle T for true or F or false for each of the following sentences.

T F 1. When a writer states a cause, he or she must be sure it is not too simple or too general.

T F 2. Time order is the only appropriate choice for arranging the supporting details in cause and effect writing.

B. Read each of the following pairs of topics for a paragraph or an essay. Which of the two would be a more effective topic to develop by cause and effect? Circle the letter of your choice.

1. a. why some people are shy
    b. effects of my shyness on my social life

2. a. three benefits of shopping for sweaters from a catalog
    b. three different styles of sweaters that can keep a person warm

3. a. reasons for child abuse
    b. reasons that Uncle Jerry sought counseling

4. a. how careful planning helped me enjoy my own party
    b. how to plan a great Halloween party

5. a. why people lie
    b. effects my boyfriend's lying had on our relationship

C. In each of the following, circle the letter of the main idea sentence that would be more effective in a cause and effect paragraph or essay. Do not choose a sentence if it is not logical, if it is too broad, or if it does not lend itself to development by the cause and effect method.

1. a. Everyone knows that violent movies have caused many of the problems in our schools today.
    b. My cousin and her husband decided to home school their son for three reasons.

2. a. Moving to a small town will change my life in several ways, for better as well as for worse.
    b. Moving to a small town would mean that I would live in a smaller house.

3. a. The effects of drug abuse on the minds of young people are tragic.
    b. My doctor changed my allergy prescription for several reasons, and the results have been satisfactory.

4. a. Students who never study make their choice not to study for one of three reasons.
    b. I have observed that I eat for several reasons, not only because I'm hungry.

D. In each blank in the following sentences, write a transitional word that will help make the combination of ideas coherent.

1. _____ Mark and Jill had stayed up late with the new baby, they did not get up early to go to the Farmers' Market.

2. One _____ of the extremely cold weather was that the local hardware store ran out of space heaters.

E. Use your imagination to do the following prewriting for a cause and effect paper. In the blanks to the left, list three possible <u>causes</u> for the topic in the center, and in the blanks to the right, list three possible <u>effects</u>.

1.

Causes   Effects

_____   _____

_____   BUYING A NEW   _____

_____   CAR   _____

2.

Causes   Effects

_____   _____

_____   QUITTING SMOKING   _____

_____   _____

F. Number each of the following support point sentences to show which sentence should be placed first (1), second, (2) and so on.

1. Several factors influenced Larry's decision to volunteer for the Big Brother program after he graduated from college.
    _____ When Larry turned fifteen, his uncle moved into town and began to spend time with him.
    _____ Having two older sisters also made him miss having male companionship.
    _____ The biggest reason was that Larry was raised by a single mother, so he knew what it was like not to have a male adult around.
    _____ His uncle's death last year caused Larry to want to give some other youngster the benefit of a caring adult male in his life.
    _____ Larry knew that if he hadn't spent time with his uncle, he might have chosen the wrong kind of male role model.

G. In the appropriate spaces below each of the following thesis statements, write the cause and the effect contained in the sentence.

1. Mr. Tucker had worked with asbestos siding in his early years as a carpenter; consequently, he developed lung problems late in life.

    cause _____

    effect _____

2. Due to an outbreak of a virus that made passengers very ill, the cruise ship company canceled three of its trips in order to clean the ship thoroughly.

    cause _____

    effect _____

H. Read the following paragraph and answer the questions.

Edie Taylor is one of a sizable number of women truck drivers on the highways today. After thirty years, however, Edie has decided to change careers for several reasons. Although she enjoyed driving a truck for years, she no longer enjoys being on the road. When she first started driving, there were few truck stops with women's shower rooms. One reason she wants to change jobs is that the sluggish economy has forced her partner Ben and her to keep the truck running constantly, without a chance to relax for a few days between trips as they did in previous years. Also, because of new technology, the company's headquarters can constantly track them by satellite or contact them via email; consequently, they feel that they are continually "on call." The main factor in Edie's decision is her age. As she approaches fifty, she finds herself more interested in slowing down and being near her aging parents than in seeing the country. Therefore, Edie has decided that her driving days are over and that her next job will be one she can do close to home.

1. Underline the topic sentence of the paragraph.

2. Cross out the one sentence that is not in unity with the rest of the paragraph.

3. Which of the following does the development of this paragraph provide?
    a. causes
    b. effects

4. Which of the following describes the order used to achieve coherence?
    a. order of importance
    b. time order

5. Circle three transitional words that help with coherence in the paragraph.

A. **Circle the letter of the choice that best answers the following questions.**

1. In argumentative (also called persuasive) writing, which of the following is NOT a possible purpose?
   a. give the reader information that will increase his or her understanding
   b. change the reader's opinion about an issue
   c. convince the reader to take action

2. Which of the following is NOT an opportunity to use persuasion?
   a. explain the rules of lacrosse to a prospective player
   b. request a loan from your parents
   c. recommend a candidate for the school board election

B. **Circle T for true or F for false for each of the following statements.**

T F 1. It is essential to consider your audience carefully when planning an argument.

T F 2. To argue effectively, a writer should appeal to the reader's emotions, especially fear, pity or vanity.

T F 3. Persuasive writing focuses primarily on solutions to problems or issues.

C. **Read each of the following pairs of topics for a paragraph or an essay. Which of the two would be better suited to argumentative, also known as persuasive, writing? Circle the letter of your choice.**

1. a. the likely characteristics of the high school classroom of the future
   b. making a case for all classrooms at a local school to be connected to the Internet

2. a. how to use the resources in the library effectively
   b. why each student should have a laptop computer

3. a. cell phones must be banned from classrooms
   b. cell phone etiquette in social settings and public places

4. a. sex education belongs at home
   b. the various mistaken ideas kids get about sex

D. **In each of the following, circle the letter of the sentence that would make a better position statement or main point for an argumentative paragraph or essay.**

1. a. The school newspaper has too many boring articles.
   b. The school newspaper ought to be published once every other week rather than once a week as it is now.

2. a. Classical or bluegrass music is all one ever hears on the radio in this town.
   b. The local public radio station should increase its variety of music programming.

3. a. A person should have to pass a test before being allowed to get married.
   b. Most marriages of teenagers result in divorce.

4. a. The people whose opinions I respect most told me to vote for Kermit Millstone.
   b. Candidate Sherry Nelson Dehart has the best qualifications for city council.

E. **The writer of an argumentative essay can use several strategies to make a case. Some of these are listed and lettered below. Included in the list is an illogical argument. Match each lettered type of evidence to the sentences that follow.**

   A. Present compelling facts
   B. Refer to an authority
   C. Predict consequences
   D. Provide pertinent examples
   E. Acknowledge and refute (or answer) the opposition
   F. Illogical

   To argue that the yield sign at the western exit of campus should be changed to a stop sign:

   1. _____ The highway patrol office that serves our campus reported fourteen minor accidents last month alone at the intersection.

   2. _____ The stop sign erected two years ago at a similarly sized college in the next county has been credited with reducing accidents.

   3. _____ Nobody even slows down, much less looks carefully, at the end of that road.

   4. _____ Without more incentive for each driver to stop and look, accidents will continue, especially after the increase in enrollment that is expected next fall.

   5. _____ Some students maintain that a stop sign would slow down the flow of traffic as students leave around 12:00, and that may be true, but the current delays caused by confusion and near misses are equally frustrating.

   6. _____ Dr. Elliott, the vice president whose home is on the opposite side of Campus Drive, is eager to represent the College in an appeal for the change to the Town Council's transportation committee.

F. **In the following items, write a K for keep or a D for drop beside each possible point to include in a persuasive essay arguing for a reduction in student ticket price to the campus theater.**

   1. _____ Student activity fees already support the college programs, including the theater.

   2. _____ Lots of students hate the idea of paying $12 a ticket for a community college play.

   3. _____ The theater has a new costume designer who used to live in New York.

4. ____ When the tickets were reduced for a special show last semester, four area high school drama classes attended, and overall sales exceeded those of the previous production which had higher prices.

5. ____ The last two plays I saw were not worth the price of admission.

G. Write a statement that presents an arguable view on one of the issues below:

Capital punishment
Requiring a foreign language for all liberal arts students
Immigration laws
Dress codes for high schools

_____

_____

_____

A. Circle the letter of the choice that best answers the following questions.

1. Which of the following is NOT an example of argument or persuasion?
    a. a telemarketer's sales call
    b. a letter from a charity urging you to donate
    c. a report on an article from the *Wall Street Journal* for your business class

2. Which of the following is NOT a technique useful in argumentative writing?
    a. acknowledgment of and response to possible objections to an idea
    b. personal attacks on those who hold the opposing view
    c. facts and statistics that support a writer's position

B. Circle T for true or F for false for each of the following statements.

T F 1. In persuasive writing, it is only important to present reasons from your experience, rather than consider what the opposing views could be.

T F 2. Reasons supporting your position should be presented logically, with verification from well-established fact or authority.

T F 3. A writer who intends to persuade the reader must make his position or opinion clear from the beginning in the main idea sentence.

C. Read each of the following pairs of topics for a paragraph or an essay. Which of the two would be better suited to argumentative or persuasive writing? Circle the letter of your choice.

1. a. the cycle of colors in the perennial plants in my garden
    b. a gardener should plant perennials rather than annuals

2. a. asking neighbors to donate toward a new community playground
    b. the unexpected kindness of a neighbor

3. a. successful time management and study habits
    b. proposal to require all new students to take an orientation course

4. a. the need for stricter home day care licensing laws in your state
    b. how you enjoyed touring your child's school on a recent visit

D. In each of the following, circle the letter of the sentence that would make a better position statement or main point for an argumentative paragraph or essay.

1. a. Dr. Wagner is the best choice for this year's Excellence in Teaching award.
    b. I have always preferred women professors to men.

2. a. My first date with the man I eventually married was a disaster.
    b. The Internet should never be used as a dating service.

3. a. Changes in airport security have caused long lines and flight delays recently.
   b. For air travel to be safer, high standards for hiring security personnel must be instituted.

4. a. Free, confidential AIDS testing should be more accessible at our county's clinic.
   b. Learning about risk factors may help reduce the likelihood of AIDS.

E. The writer of an argumentative essay can use several strategies to make a case. Some of these are listed and lettered below. Included in the list is an argument. Match each lettered type of evidence to the sentences that follow.

    A. Present compelling facts
    B. Refer to an authority
    C. Predict consequences
    D. Provide pertinent examples
    E. Acknowledge and refute the opposition
    F. Illogical

For an argument that the college should build a new parking lot or a parking deck:

1. _____ The cost of a new parking lot is a valid concern, but the investment would yield results in the end. The college would be able to accommodate more students in morning classes, which is the most popular time of day; furthermore, the salary of the extra officer required now to direct incoming traffic could be saved.

2. _____ People who arrive for 10:00 a.m. classes are fools since they have to walk half a mile from the empty office building lot down the street.

3. _____ Unless more parking is provided, many students may decide to attend the community college in the next county, which is only twenty miles away with plenty of free parking.

4. _____ According to Chief Collins, whose department keeps a record of the ratio of parking spaces to cars, the college has not been able to ticket for illegal parking for three years now because there is literally no other place for those students to park. The college has therefore lost the income that such ticketing would have generated.

5. _____ The parking deck at the state art museum added over one hundred spaces to the capacity and allowed the designation of ten more handicapped spaces.

6. _____ By 8:30 every Monday, Wednesday, and Friday this fall, every single parking space on campus was occupied, so students had to park on the hill beside the gym.

F. **In the following items, write a K for keep or a D for drop beside each possible point to include in a persuasive essay arguing that the reader should discard organic garbage in a compost pile for use in his or her garden.**

1. _____ Food waste biodegrades to become excellent, fertile soil.

2. _____ Using composted soil to fertilize your garden will guarantee great results.

3. _____ The unpleasant, sometimes bothersome odor from rotting compost can be greatly reduced if the compost pile is not allowed to remain too wet.

4. _____ My mother, who has a Master Gardener certificate, uses compost, so it really works.

5. _____ Everybody I know hates to use commercial fertilizers, which may contain chemicals harmful to bugs.

G. **Write a statement that presents an arguable view on <u>one</u> of the issues below:**

Employers providing daycare
Attendance policy at the college you attend
The movie rating system
Drug testing

_____

_____

_____

PART III

Sentence Skills, Grammar, and Mechanics

A.   **In each of the following sentences, underline the verb twice and circle the subject. It may help to cross out prepositional phrases.**

1. The old dock at the lake needs some repairs.

2. My neighbors bought a large truck and parked it in their front yard.

3. Movie critics in the newspaper gave that film a positive review.

4. Most of the fast food restaurants in town are offering toys in their kids' meals.

5. Are the runners ready for the track meet?

6. Tan had been working on her algebra homework for several hours.

7. The design of the new kitchen is modern and functional.

8. A cruise around Manhattan is both entertaining and educational.

9. My uncle's stay in the hospital lasted for a week.

10. The atmosphere surrounding the day care center is a safe and nurturing one.

11. Tim and Vickie have just moved from their trailer to a new condo in the city.

12. Does the psychology instructor accept late reports?

13. Contrary to the opinion of my friends, my life does not revolve around my girlfriend.

14. At my job as a teacher's assistant, I enjoy greeting the children every day.

15. The director of the play always gives the actors good advice and advises them about the motivations for their characters.

B.   **In the following sentences, mark the sentence parts in these ways:**
- **underline the verb twice**
- **circle the subject**
- **draw a box around the word that completes the idea (This word is a direct object or another kind of completer.)**
- **put parentheses around prepositional phrases.**

1. Her husband respected her decision to return to college.

2. My grandfather was a first-rate carpenter.

3. Tony and Isaac have not yet bought the tickets for the concert.

4. My sister's family enjoys kayaking on the rivers of this beautiful state.

5. Free admission to movies is an advantage of my job at the concession stand.

C. **In each of the following sentences, mark the sentences as you did above in Part B. In these, however, also do the following labeling step:**
- **write M for modifier above all the words that describe the subject, verb, and completer.**

1. An old homeless man slowly walked along the railroad tracks.

2. The local community college will soon begin a new semester.

3. The patient's faithful friend paced around the waiting room during the operation.

4. A nutritious breakfast is the most important meal of the day.

5. The beautiful rays of the sunrise are lighting the orange canyon walls.

A. **In each of the following sentences, underline the verb twice and circle the subject. It may help to cross out prepositional phrases.**

1. One of the staff members of the museum noticed something surprising on the floor.

2. Harry and Nan recently closed their house for the winter and flew to Florida.

3. Has anyone seen my copy of the English textbook?

4. Most of the early spring flowers are just now beginning to bloom.

5. Walking is excellent exercise for good health.

6. The engineers' plans were submitted to the committee and accepted without revision.

7. Both of those math instructors are usually working in their offices by 7:30 a.m.

8. There was no more room for latecomers in the auditorium.

9. The swaying trees reminded Monique of dancers.

10. Did the students finish the independent project on time?

11. Fern's natural speaking ability and her desire to help others have led her to a career in the ministry.

12. After a few months, some of my friends will be moving to Salt Lake City.

13. Grace has recently begun to accept too many credit cards in the mail.

14. The newest nurses working in the clinic were given name tags for the blood drive.

15. The claims of that cleaning product sound too good to be true.

B. **In the following sentences, mark the sentence parts in these ways:**
- **underline the verb twice**
- **circle the subject**
- **draw a box around the word that completes the idea (This word is a direct object or another kind of completer.)**
- **put parentheses around prepositional phrases.**

1. Ernesto squeezed the toothpaste tube to get the remaining contents out.

2. The old photograph shows a prairie family on the front porch of a cabin.

3. The members of the jury did not receive adequate instructions.

4. My wealthy cousin can certainly afford a good set of golf clubs.

5. The spaghetti sauce in the yellow bowl tastes too salty.

C. **In each of the following sentences, mark the sentences as you did above in Part B. In these, however, also do the following labeling step:**
   - **write M for modifier above all the words that describe the subject, verb, and completer.**

1. The trail guide led the tired but happy group up the steep hill to the lodge.

2. The clothes dryer in the laundry room emitted a loud humming sound.

3. Cracked and uneven concrete covered the former patio area in her backyard.

4. The sweet familiar smell of lilacs was a nice welcome home.

5. Is your grandfather clock a valuable antique?

A. **In the blanks, write C if the sentence uses coordination and S if it uses subordination. Then circle the conjunction that is used to join or subordinate ideas.**

1. _____ Sonia wants to buy a useful gift for her neighbor's wedding shower, but she has no idea what the couple needs.

2. _____ If you are determined to go to the concert, you'll have to work extra hours to earn money for the tickets.

3. _____ We found some people in our assigned seats when we got to the game.

4. _____ Greg enjoys all water sports, so his dream is to move to the beach.

5. _____ After she finished her test, Lashonda began working on the homework.

B **Add commas as needed in the sentences below. If a sentence does not need a comma, write "none" in the right margin.**

1. Kendall had lost her gloves and her hands were turning blue with the cold. _____

2. You should shampoo your hair after swimming in chlorinated water. _____

3. Unless it rains we expect to go on a long hike this Saturday. _____

4. The teacher was attending a conference for two days so she left lessons and assignments for her class to do in her absence. _____

5. Dr. Lee works at the clinic on Mondays and at the hospital the rest of the week. _____

6. Although Gustavo usually goes home for lunch today he ate in the cafeteria. _____

7. People tend to remember the same things over and over as they get older. _____

C. **Combine the following sets of ideas using either coordination or subordination. Write out your combinations completely. Be sure to add the necessary punctuation.**

1. Shelly loves shrimp and oysters.
   She is allergic to all kinds of shellfish.

2. Grapes are among the oldest cultivated plants.
   They are mentioned in many ancient myths and fables.

3. We had trouble finding an apartment.
   We owned three cats and two dogs.

4. The artist known as El Greco was born in Greece.
   He did most of his painting in Spain.

5. Dave quit his job at the restaurant.
   He found another job making more money.

6. Queen Elizabeth II came to England's throne in February, 1952.
   Her coronation was in June of the following year.

7. Organizers were forced to cancel the parade.
   A blizzard dumped three feet of snow overnight.

8. Laura washed the dishes.
   William put the leftovers in the refrigerator.

D. Write a sentence using each of the following conjunctions. Write out your sentence completely, and punctuate as necessary.

1. or

2. until

3. before

E. **For the next two pairs of ideas, write two combinations. In the first, use coordination. In the second, use subordination.**

1. Jorge turned on the air conditioner.
   The car remained hot.

   a. using coordination:

   b. using subordination:

2. Ben and his brother both enjoy exploring the river.
   They took a kayaking class together.

   a. using coordination:

   b. using subordination:

A. **In the blanks, write C if the sentence uses coordination and S if it uses subordination. Then circle the conjunction that is used to join or subordinate ideas.**

1. _____ I drove slowly through the storm, for I could barely see the road ahead.

2. _____ My kids were very anxious after they heard about the robbery last night.

3. _____ Because I had so much housework to do, I never even turned on the TV.

4. _____ The driest place in America is in Nevada, and the wettest is in Hawaii.

5. _____ You will be so tired if you stay up to watch that movie.

B. **Add commas as needed in the sentences below. If a sentence does not need a comma, write "none" in the right margin.**

1. Some towns are named for geographical features and others for other older towns. _____

2. As the actors came out for the curtain call audience members rose to their feet. _____

3. Isabel wasn't sleepy but she made herself a cup of coffee just in case. _____

4. Hank had no choice but to wait in the long line because he had to buy diapers for the baby. _____

5. The new job has long hours but excellent pay so I have decided to take it. _____

6. Do not judge a person until you have walked a mile in his or her shoes. _____

7. Even though the drycleaners ruined my suit they did not offer to pay for it. _____

C. **Combine the following sets of ideas using either coordination or subordination. Write out your combinations completely. Be sure to add the necessary punctuation.**

1. Greg is studying theater.
   His parents had urged him to major in business.

2. The twins are tired of being mistaken for each other.
   They intend to transfer to colleges in different towns.

3. Wendy can tell that the pollen count is high.
   Her eyes have been watering all day.

4. Dr. Thomas heard about the accident on the radio.
   She rushed to the emergency room.

5. Helen set the table for dinner.
   Marty took the bread out of the oven.

6. Lee works out at the gym daily.
   He wants to lose ten pounds before his wedding.

7. Mark gave his girlfriend a necklace.
   The necklace had belonged to his grandmother.

8. Olivia quit her job.
   She was making a good salary.

D. **Write a sentence using each of the following conjunctions. Write out your combination completely, and punctuate as necessary.**

1. although

2. for

3. unless

E. For the next two pairs of ideas, write two combinations. In the first, use coordination. In the second, use subordination.

1. Nell wants to take a vacation to Florida.
    She has never been there.

    a. using coordination:

    b. using subordination:

2. Boston is an interesting, historic city.
    The winters can be severe.

    a. using coordination:

    b. using subordination:

A.   **In the blank, write S if the group of words is a sentence and F if it is a fragment.**

1. _____ One of the funniest TV shows on the air today.

2. _____ Either Simon or his dad will repair the broken table.

3. _____ Standing by the bus stop in the rain with no umbrella.

4. _____ The amount of practice, discipline, and effort to become a superstar.

5. _____ If I did the right thing according to my conscience.

6. _____ The bell rang to call the campers to dinner.

7. _____ While Kevin painted the living room ceiling.

8. _____ During class, someone quietly left.

9. _____ The weather which turned much colder over the weekend.

10. _____ Ships loaded with cargo from South America.

11. _____ Asleep at the foot of the bed lay a white cat.

12. _____ Especially the kind of Oreo with the chocolate cream in the middle.

13. _____ Terry laughed out loud.

14. _____ With love in her heart, she released the bird back into the wild.

15. _____ Rowing a boat slowly beside the island's shoreline.

B.   **Rewrite the fragments below to change them into sentences.**

1. The tall man waiting in the lobby _____

_____

2. Pulled a muscle while she was raking leaves _____

_____

3. In spite of the terrible weather _____

_____

4. The woman who just walked into the room _____

_____

5. Staring at the clock _____

_____

C. **The following paragraph contains five fragments. Underline each one. Make clear editing marks that show how you would correct these fragments. You may cross out words, add words above the line, or change punctuation marks.**

A counselor once told me something that surprised me at the time. But which I later realized was true. I had told her that I wished I had someone to take care of me. She told me if I did not learn to take care of myself. No one else ever would. At the time, I did not like hearing this. Feeling that it was a harsh thing to say. As I learned more about the challenges of life. I learned that a person really does need to take care of herself. I eventually went back to visit the wise counselor who had taught me a valuable lesson. To thank her for telling me the truth.

A.   In the blank, write S if the group of words is a sentence and F if it is a fragment.

1. ____ Posing on the steps outside the Capitol with their American flags.

2. ____ The holes in the fabric are intended to let it "breathe" moisture out, away from the body.

3. ____ Many myths exist about the way the early settlers lived.

4. ____ Despite my best efforts to come up with a suitable topic for my essay.

5. ____ Several of the boxes of telephone line wet from being left in the rain.

6. ____ Offices opened in order for the air ducts to be cleaned while we were away.

7. ____ Lying in the bottom of the large gift bag was a tiny box wrapped in white.

8. ____ The degree to which some people will go to avoid work.

9. ____ Knowing the hammock might be ruined in the rainstorm, she brought it inside.

10. ____ At the end of the narrow dead-end road on my neighbor's property.

11. ____ The camp where my sister spent five summers in a row.

12. ____ Teenagers often complain about vacations with their parents.

13. ____ The driver just stared ahead.

14. ____ Until all of the books are replaced where they belong.

15. ____ But never at the end of a party when the clean up work begins.

B.   Rewrite the fragments below to change them into sentences. Add punctuation where needed.

1. As soon as I get to the building site _____

_____

2. Using a new software program to produce the newsletter _____

_____

3. Whether or not the repair work on his car will be finished _____

_____

4. One of the students who was carrying a protest sign _____

   _____

5. The stove that I picked out to go in the remodeled kitchen _____

   _____

C. **The following paragraph contains five fragments. Underline each one. Make clear editing marks that show how you would correct these fragments. You may cross out words, add words above the line, or change punctuation marks.**

   The Learning Resources Center on the main campus is in disarray this summer. Because the walls are being painted and the carpet is being replaced. Workers began by moving all the stacks of books. In order to work around them. They started with the first floor during the break between spring and summer terms. After classes began for the summer, the LRC had to be closed. But only for three days while the first floor circulation area was painted and carpeted. The biggest complaint about the work was the loss of the computer lab. Which had to be shut down for two weeks due to water damage. This had to be fixed. Before the new carpet could be laid. Now all the areas of the LRC are back in service, and the staff and students are enjoying the fresh new surroundings.

A. In the blank to the left, label each group of words. Write S if it is a sentence, RO if it is a run-on, and CS if it is a comma splice. Then in the space below, write a correction for each RO or CS. Write out your correction completely.

1. _____ Most American chestnut trees in the South died in the 1920s botanists are breeding hybrids to return them to the forests.

2. _____ Barbara realized that she had a long drive the next day, she set her clock for 4:30 a.m.

3. _____ Spicy foods give my dad heartburn, especially those that contain peppers.

4. _____ One reason to attend community colleges is an economic one, tuition costs usually are much lower than those for universities.

5. _____ Showing off to the substitute instructor, Mark made a rude remark that his classmates did not appreciate.

6. _____ Eastwood High's varsity baseball team won the semifinals now they will compete in the state championship.

7. _____ The United Nations was formed from an earlier organization called the League of Nations.

8. _____ Take care of the little things, the large things will take care of themselves.

9. _____ Please take this paper to Nell she needs it for her graphic art portfolio.

10. _____ "The Little Red Hen" is a famous children's story it teaches the importance of working for rewards.

11. _____ The average temperature in Costa Rica is warm, the climate there is perfect for a vacation any time of year.

12. _____ Dorothy locked her dog Speedy into the laundry room while she entertained her bridge club.

13. ____ The boss had an important announcement to make, she called a meeting in the conference room.

14. ____ Emma and Lou are planning a trip to Los Angeles to help their nephew move into a new apartment.

15. ____ Distance education classes offer a lot of convenience they also demand a lot of self-discipline.

B. Correct the following sentence mistake in four ways. Write out each correction completely.

Gil locked his keys in the car this morning, he was late for work.

1.

2.

3.

4.

C. The following paragraph has six sentence mistakes in it. Each mistake is a run-on or a comma splice. At each spot where two complete ideas come together incorrectly, make a correction.

Todd's aging mother has had to make some changes lately because of her physical condition. She had back surgery a few months ago now she has to have another operation. Todd and his wife are trying to help his mother accept the fact that she can't do everything she used to do. For example, she has always valued a clean house, she never had anyone help her with housework. Recently, Todd hired someone to clean. His mother had tried to vacuum the floors herself, that's one reason her back didn't heal well. She objected at first to using a cane, she finally gave in and started using one, it helps her get around. The entire family has high hopes that the next surgery will ease the pain Todd's mother will have to follow doctor's orders if she is going to get well.

AVOIDING RUN-ONS AND COMMA SPLICES   **Test B**

A.   **In the blank to the left, label each group of words. Write S if it is a sentence, RO if it is a run-on, and CS if it is a comma splice. Then in the space below, write a correction for each RO or CS. Write out your correction completely.**

1. _____ Salt is a spice that we use every day we seldom think about where it comes from.

2. _____ It comes from mines, from wells, from springs, from salt lakes, and, as most of us realize, from the sea.

3. _____ Salt water is known as brine, it can be boiled to make salt which is the result when the water evaporates.

4. _____ Another way to get salt from brine is to let the water stand in the sun in big shallow ponds.

5. _____ The sun dries the water away, the salt stays behind.

6. _____ Sometimes an underground stream flows through a bed of salt when it comes to the surface, it is a salt spring.

7. _____ The tunnels of a salt mine sparkle like ice, using drills, miners cut the solid salt away in great glistening chunks.

8. _____ Then power shovels scoop it up and load it into railroad cars which haul it out of the mine.

9. _____ In ancient times, salt was scarce, only people who lived near the sea could get it easily.

10. _____ Salt was essential to preserve meat and fish there were no means of refrigeration.

11. _____ Salt was so valuable that it was used as money, the Latin word *salarium*, which was payment in salt, is the basis for our modern word *salary*.

12. _____ One of the earliest trade roads in the world, the Via Salaria from Ostia to Rome, was developed because of salt.

13. _____ At one time, salt even had religious significance, it was a symbol of purity.

14. _____ The ancient Hebrews had a custom of rubbing newborn babies with salt they thought it would ensure good health.

15. _____ In modern times, salt has been used as a sign of friendship and hospitality.

B. Correct the following sentence mistake in four ways. Write out each correction completely.

Liz and her mother have a close relationship, they live hundreds of miles apart.

1.

2.

3.

4.

C. The following paragraph has six sentence mistakes in it. Each one is a run-on or a comma splice. At each spot where two complete ideas come together incorrectly, make a correction.

All over the United States, many people have a growing concern about the number of violent crimes committed by young people. Parents and teachers can watch for certain warning signals, any child or teenager whose life shows danger signs may need help. First, a young person needs to have a parent or caring adult in his or her life, someone to confide in and listen to. This person does not necessarily have to be a parent, it may be another relative or mentor. The caring adult should be concerned about any child who is frequently angry or depressed he or she must observe whether the child is treated badly by peers. Caregivers usually know to be concerned about the company their children keep. Negative influences can cause a young person to go astray if he or she admires the "bad guys" too much, the misplaced admiration can lead to problems. There is a fine line between fascination with violent games, movies, and music and imagining doing violence. Failure in school is a warning signal, the child may look for success in another area. Access to and fascination with weapons is a warning sign that a child may be in danger of developing a tendency toward violence. Americans have a duty to pay attention to the lives of children, lives and futures could be saved.

A.   Circle the correct form of the verb.

1.   Two months ago, Arnold (become, became) an uncle for the first time.

2.   Rolf's music appreciation instructor (did, done) a lot to help him with his project.

3.   After the burglary, Derek (had, have) to get a new alarm system.

4.   By midnight last night, we had (ate, eaten) the entire box of cookies.

5.   My former baseball coach (teaches, taught) me a lesson I have always valued.

6.   Most of the seafood on the buffet was already (went, gone) by the time I got there.

7.   I didn't understand what the teacher (means, meant) by those strange comments.

8.   If the paper is (tore, torn), it will not be accepted by the teacher.

9.   Have the autumn leaves (fell, fallen) from the large oak trees in the park?

10.   Recently, Keisha and her family (began, begun) packing for their move to Alaska.

11.   The children's choir (sang, sung) a hymn for the Mother's Day church service.

12.   Mr. Lattimore told us that he has (knew, known) our family for many years.

13.   The storm could cause a power outage that might spoil our (froze, frozen) foods.

14.   Tamika missed her bus because she had (took, taken) so long getting ready.

15.   Marie promised her friend that she (will, would) write him during the summer.

16.   As the sun set on the hills, the wind (makes, made) an eerie sound.

17.   Frances couldn't tape the news since her VCR (has, had) broken the night before.

18.   Her message said, "I can't come to the phone now; I (am, was) washing my hair."

19.   The letter, which her son had (wrote, written) from overseas, was kept in the family Bible.

20.   Marco intends to (continue, continuing) his studies in Michigan next spring.

B. **Revise the following sentences to change the verb from passive to active.**

1. The diagram on the chart was drawn by the chemistry professor.

2. Several unusual pieces of pottery have been found by the student archaeologists.

3. The kids in my son's class are being taken to the zoo by four of the parents.

C. **Revise the verb mistake in the following sentences. Each sentence has one word that needs to be changed. Cross out the mistake and write a correction above the line.**

1. Aunt Annie was pleased that her son come to visit her in the nursing home.

2. My cousins thought that my new car costed more than it actually did.

A. Circle the correct form of the verb.

1. Ralph thought that he had (did, done) well on the presentation, so he was confident about getting the account.

2. Diane has always been polite and (treat, treated) her teachers with respect.

3. Are you sure you (saw, seen) Monique with Shane last night?

4. The rest of the committee has not (began, begun) working on the report.

5. I have always (drove, driven) a large car, and high gas prices won't stop me now.

6. The class has not (went, gone) as well as the professor hoped it would.

7. The article she (wrote, written) for the newspaper raised some good questions.

8. Denise's parents are proud that she has (become, became) a graphic designer.

9. Has Derek always (ate, eaten) such a big lunch and a small dinner?

10. Fay was familiar with the anthem that was (sang, sung) during the ceremony.

11. Sally has, on occasion, (drank, drunk) a bit too much wine and regretted it later.

12. The Leonards have (gave, given) their old truck to Habitat for Humanity.

13. Mrs. Stanley has finally (chose, chosen) the wallpaper for her new bathroom.

14. While I finish making the gravy, (will, would) you please set the table for dinner?

15. As Angie watched her son play soccer, she (is, was) thinking of her mother.

16. Before the carolers left the church, they (have, had) all put on hats and scarves.

17. Sue found her old hair dryer while she (looked, was looking) for the toolbox.

18. Last summer, Brandy (earned, had earned) enough extra money to buy her boyfriend a nice birthday gift.

19. I (have wanted, had wanted) a new stereo for a year now; I can finally afford one.

20. Before the assistant went to pick up mail, he (had received, received) ten phone calls.

B. **Revise the following sentences to change the verb from passive to active.**

1. The entire anniversary dinner was prepared by Dave and Sandra's children.

2. The driving test was finally passed the third time by Grandpa.

3. Tommy's bedroom will be painted by the work crew tomorrow.

C. **Revise the verb mistake in the following sentences. Each sentence has one word that needs to be changed. Cross out the mistake and write a correction above the line.**

1. Ellen has already put my name on the list of people to be contact about the party.

2. Iris has been homesick until she finally got off the plane and greeted her husband.

A. Circle the verb that agrees with the subject in each sentence.

1. The library books on the cart in the hall (need, needs) to be reshelved.

2. Each of the recipes in that cookbook (was, were) submitted by a member of the garden club.

3. The collie and the black poodle both (belong, belongs) to the folks who live beside the park.

4. Caring for a sick child (require, requires) a great deal of patience.

5. (Has, Have) all of the uniforms been cleaned for the game?

6. Either a skateboard or a scooter (make, makes) a great gift for an active child.

7. A case of soft drinks (consist, consists) of twenty-four cans.

8. There (is, are) an application to complete before you can use the card.

9. The sign, featuring a police car with flashing lights, (read, reads), "Don't drink and drive unless you want this kind of chaser."

10. Maria is an employee who constantly (watch, watches) the clock during breaks.

11. The names of the five safest companies of the year (was, were) published in yesterday's newspaper.

12. There, in the photograph beside Tamara, (sit, sits) her faithful dog Rocky.

13. Everyone at the concert (seem, seems) eager for the main attraction to arrive.

14. The price of the repairs to the dented car (is, are) reasonable.

15. The basketball team (play, plays) each game in the community gym instead of at the local elementary school.

16. Lori and Irene, best friends since childhood, (attend, attends) college classes together.

17. (Do, Does) the movies at the downtown theater cost less for a matinee show?

B. Choose from among these verbs to complete each of the following sentences. Add the verb and enough words to make a complete idea.

look   looks   is   are   need   needs   try   tries   plan   plans

1. One of my brothers _____.

2. Sara is a woman who _____.

3. Most of the stockroom workers _____.

C. In the following paragraph, there are five subject-verb agreement mistakes. Find each one and above it, write the correct form of the verb.

Garden ornaments are increasing in popularity. Landscape nurseries these days offers more than just plants and fertilizers. Shoppers can find all kinds of objects that decorates the garden alongside the flowers. There is, for example, rocks with words written on them and stepping stones with elaborate pictures. Sculptures of various kinds provide hiding places for house keys or creates a place for birds to bathe. In my favorite garden, a six-foot dragonfly by the gate welcome visitors. Gardeners choose artistic accessories to accent the flowers and shrubs they work so hard to grow.

A. Circle the verb that agrees with the subject in each sentence.

1. Some people really (enjoy, enjoys) shopping for hours.

2. A fan of shopping (consider, considers) the activity a game or a treasure hunt.

3. On a quest, an avid shopper (go, goes) from store to store looking for just the right purchase.

4. Busy traffic, long lines, and crowded aisles (doesn't, don't) bother these folks.

5. Coming home empty handed just (give, gives) them an excuse to shop again the next day.

6. Although it's not the only way to shop, there certainly (is, are) some advantages to shopping in a store in person.

7. For one thing, a person can try on clothes before he or she (make, makes) a final decision.

8. Another reason to shop in person (is, are) to obtain a purchase immediately rather than wait for it to come in the mail.

9. This is important to anyone who (wait, waits) until the last minute to buy a birthday present.

10. However, for those who dislike shopping, there (is, are) some alternatives.

11. Mail-order catalogs (make, makes) shopping easy and convenient.

12. With a catalog and a phone, each shopper (set, sets) his or her own hours.

13. Neither congested traffic nor long lines (annoy, annoys) an "armchair shopper."

14. The Internet, with all of its e-commerce sites, also (offer, offers) shopping convenience.

15. Browsing online and buying via the Internet (help, helps) a busy person use time more efficiently.

16. Once a person begins to shop by phone, he or she (start, starts) to receive a variety of catalogs in the mail.

17. A company often (sell, sells) its mailing list to other retailers targeting similar customers.

B. Choose from among these verbs to complete each of the following sentences. Add the verb and enough other words to make a complete idea.

seem   seems   was   were   look   looks   has   have   do   does

1. Either Rita or her parents _____ .

2. The organization _____ .

3. The main reason for his fears _____ .

C. In the following paragraph, there are five subject-verb agreement mistakes. Find each one and above it, write the correct form of the verb.

How would you like to have a job that consist of nothing but washing windows? It takes workers about four months to clean the thousands of windows of the Empire State Building in New York City. Then come the hard part, which is starting all over again as soon as the job is finished. The task of cleaning the 6,500 windows are never completely done. There is a few lessons that amateurs can learn from professionals. According to the pros, the essential ingredients for a clean window includes a good squeegee, mild detergent, ammonia, water, a highly absorbent cloth, a sponge, and a razor blade.

USING PRONOUNS CORRECTLY: Test A
CASE, REFERENCE, AND CONSISTENCY

A.   **Circle the correct pronoun from the choices in each sentence.**

1. Yolanda is going with Gerald and (I, me) to the library for the book fair.

2. Were Chuck and (she, her) at the meeting last night?

3. My wife, a sports fanatic, likes football even more than (I, me).

4. (He, Him) and (I, me) are members of the same gym.

5. Dottie is not as tall as her brother, and she is much thinner than (he, him.)

6. Louise, please sit here between Aunt Lou and (I, me).

7. The minister has asked (we, us) youth leaders to present our budget.

8. When I answer the phone and am asked for the man of the house, I always say, "This is (she, her)."

9. Jessie ate a larger dinner than (I, me).

10. The company will pay travel expenses for only one of us, Mr. Hill or (I, me).

11. While driving to El Paso, Ikiko and (he, him) stopped to shop for jewelry.

12. The jacket looks better on you than (he, him).

13. Barbara's dog is better behaved than mine is, but mine is cuter than (hers, her's).

14. Will you please give Ada and (I, me) a ride home from play rehearsal?

15. The company is planning (it's, its) annual summer picnic for July 27.

B.   **Each sentence below has a problem with pronoun reference or consistency. Cross through the problem pronoun, and in the space below, rewrite the sentence to make it clearer.**

1. Ken wrote to John each day while he was in the hospital recuperation wing.

2. My son's best friend, which comes from Tulsa, is studying to be an electrician.

3. Dina commented to Martha that her dress was an old one.

4. The glass slipped out of my hand onto the ceramic tray, and it broke.

5. When the Gilberts go to their beach house, you don't need to take many household supplies.

6. At the library, they said that my book was two weeks overdue.

7. Between you and I, that poem did not deserve to win first prize.

8. Thurman, he needs a haircut and a shave if he hopes to get that job.

9. The coach asked Dmitri and myself to bring out the gloves and bats for practice.

10. No one does a better job of enforcing the attendance policy than her.

A. **Circle the correct pronoun from the choices in each sentence.**

1. Sherry and (he, him) were determined to get the singer's autograph.

2. When the elevator opened, people on their way to the game tried to push Craig and (I, me) out of the way.

3. Molly and (I, me) were the only people younger than 55 on the bus to Miami.

4. When we saw the flat tire, the boss asked Elaine and (I, me) if we needed a ride.

5. Some of the other girls and (we, us) are going to the movies tonight.

6. Lisa was angry when she realized that the clerk was insulting her dad and (her, she.)

7. Have you seen the poetry collection that Toby and (she, her) have put together?

8. There has never been any trouble between (us, we) until now.

9. Even though his friends make fun of him, Simon is better off than (they, them).

10. Ms. Maxon is great; I have never enjoyed a teacher more than (she, her).

11. One of my coworkers claims that she is much more qualified than (I, me).

12. If you want to achieve great things, (you, a person) must work hard.

13. Anyone who loves (his or her, your) work is truly rich.

14. Members of the planning committee will need (your, their) own copies of the handbook.

15. If a person wants to appreciate fine coffee, (he, you, they) must drink it black.

B. **Each sentence below has a problem with pronoun reference or consistency. Cross out the problem pronoun, and in the space below, rewrite the sentence to make it clearer.**

1. Delta announced they will lay off several hundred workers in the next year.

2. The Writing Center Director told the Dean that she was needed as an advisor for the committee.

3. I flicked on the television and sat down to channel surf, which you do sometimes just to escape.

4. Unless I make myself a list, it's hard to get errands done during your typical day off.

5. Brandon goes to the tutoring center for help in math because he finds them very patient.

6. Ann can't believe the news that her and her sister heard on the way to class.

7. The salesman at the hardware store told Steve that he didn't really know much about plumbing.

8. After braiding Marie's hair, she decorated them with ribbons.

9. I was so pleased that my granddaughter visited my husband and myself by herself.

10. The boss insists that no one is more committed to the plan than him.

A.   Circle the correct pronoun from the choices in each of the following sentences.

1.   Whenever the children fight with each other over the remote, I make (him or her, them) turn off the TV.

2.   Each of the referees for the men's game is already wearing (his, their) uniform.

3.   The boss wants all the employees to complete (his or her, their) self-evaluations by Friday.

4.   Neither of the plumbers has given me (his or her, their) estimate yet.

5.   The newest member of the orchestra, a violinist, asked (her, their) former director to attend the concert.

6.   All carpentry students must buy (his or her, their) own tools.

7.   The committee might decide to conduct (its, their) next meeting behind closed doors.

8.   Many musicians of Mozart's time learned to write music while they were young, but no one else composed (his, their) own symphony at age five.

9.   Both of the twins must clean (his, their) rooms before dinner.

10.   Each person on the jury had (his or her, their) doubts about the truthfulness of the witness.

11.   The engineers' plans were submitted to the board, but (he, it, they) had not been printed in the correct format.

12.   Anyone can enter the contest as long as (he or she, they) is at least eighteen years old.

13.   Car dealers are experts at giving you the standard pitch, but most of them really do know what (he or she, they) are talking about.

14.   The club has made plans to hold (its, their) meetings on Wednesdays at noon next semester.

15.   Neither the president nor the employees wore (her, their) usual business attire the day the company moved.

B.   Write a correct pronoun in the blank in the following sentences.

1.   One of the boys at camp has written _____ parents every single day.

2.   The average customer at the bank has _____ savings in different kinds of accounts.

3. The governing board of the YMCA approved the minutes from _____ June meeting.

4. A husband and a wife often review how _____ days have gone after the kids have gone to bed.

5. Each of the members of the men's basketball team must buy _____ own shoes.

6. Neither Mary nor Felicia has _____ own car.

7. Books and magazines had been removed from _____ proper storage places and were scattered all over the room.

8. The company advertised _____ annual picnic for the same day as the consultant's visit.

9. If anyone has a question about _____ insurance, a representative from the company will be here tomorrow.

10. The library had been recently remodeled, but _____ periodicals collection still needed updating.

A.   Circle the correct pronoun from the choices in each of the following sentences.

1. It's amazing how each leaf can be identified by (its, their) own pattern of veins.

2. Can any woman ever forget the first time (she, they) fell in love?

3. Everybody on the swim team jumped into the pool to practice (his, their) back stroke.

4. Neither Brad nor Dan answers (his, their) telephone before 10:00 a.m.

5. Each of the nominated essays had (its, their) good points; agreeing on which was the best was a difficult task for the judges.

6. Allen, like most of the other auto mechanics students, wrote (his, their) process essay about cars.

7. Both Bob and Carrie have trouble keeping control of (her, their) credit cards.

8. That newspaper is known for (its, their) honest and thorough reporting on crime.

9. Either Mr. Adams or Mr. Bradshaw will help you in any way that (he, they) can.

10. A student must be committed to doing the best (he or she, they) can or tuition money is wasted.

11. This collection of photographs is traveling around the state on (its, their) way to New York.

12. Those two students failed the course because neither of them did (her, their) term paper.

13. Employees on educational leave will continue to receive (his or her, their) benefits.

14. The flock of Canada geese is ready to make (its, their) annual journey south.

15. If anyone is against this marriage, let (him or her, them) speak now.

B.   Write a correct pronoun in the blank in the following sentences.

1. Any student can get help from the tutoring center if _____ asks for it.

2. You cannot always judge a book by _____ cover.

3. Most Americans eat more carbohydrates than _____ should.

4. A person can get as much benefit from regular walking as _____ can from jogging.

5. The college is planning _____ annual campaign to the alumni for donations.

6. I realize that this is not the most suitable living arrangement that _____ could have chosen.

7. Each company representative will vote on _____ choice for the convention location for next year.

8. The committee had already planned _____ agenda for the March meeting before I could be scheduled to bring my concerns to the meeting.

9. No one can really say what _____ would do under the same circumstances.

10. Any teacher can improve _____ effectiveness by becoming familiar with the specific needs of _____ students.

USING MODIFIERS CORRECTLY   Test A
ADJECTIVES AND ADVERBS, MODIFIER PROBLEMS

A. Circle the correct choice of the modifier in the parentheses.

1. Jason watched (quiet, quietly) from his hiding place behind the sofa.

2. The principal wrote a (sincere, sincerely) letter thanking her staff for their hard work.

3. Please give Vimla back her dishes, and thank her for that (delicious, deliciously) meal.

4. Gail is not a (mature, maturely) person, but she works (good, well) independently.

5. The sentence was not written (clear, clearly) enough for me to understand it.

6. Two large bodyguards stood (patient, patiently) beside the door to the room.

7. Leslie was a dedicated and (diligent, diligently) worker.

8. Violets need just the right amount of water and light to grow (good, well).

9. Tess is hungry, but her brother is (hungrier, hungriest) than she is.

10. My dad had the (most large, largest) hands I ever saw.

11. Which one of the seven dwarfs was the (smaller, smallest)?

12. Of Neal's two dogs, Chance is the (heavier, heaviest).

13. This has been the (rainier, rainiest) spring we have had for at least nine years.

14. I always did (good, well) at avoiding trouble, certainly (better, best) than my sister did.

15. Jan was (real, really) sorry about arriving late at her supervisor's wedding.

B. Each of the following sentences contains one error in adjective or adverb form. Cross out the mistake and right the correct word above the line.

1. The dinner was burned so bad that we couldn't eat it.

2. Which class would be hardest for you, psychology or sociology?

3. Mothers should handle their babies gentle because the babies' skulls are so fragile.

4. We've had several mean coaches lately, but Ms. Nichols is the worse.

C. **Write in the correct form of the adjective or adverb in parentheses.**

1. Stella is (gracious) _____ about losing than Jenny is.

2. John F. Kennedy was one of the (popular) _____ presidents this country has ever had.

3. That restaurant served the (bad) _____ soup I ever tasted.

D. **Each of the following sentences has an underlined modifier phrase next to it. Write a combination that puts the modifier where it belongs in the original sentence. Write out your new sentence completely.**

1. Ted looked around the living room nervously.   <u>waiting for his date to come downstairs</u>

2. Bill gave his sweetheart a necklace as they watched the sunset.   <u>that he had made himself</u>

3. I could see the mechanic working on my car.   <u>covered in grease and grime</u>

A. **Circle the correct choice of the modifier in the parentheses.**

1. The dinner hour at the Stevens' house is rarely (peaceful, peacefully).

2. Many older drivers drive (slow, slowly) because they aren't in a hurry to get anywhere.

3. If I get the raise I asked for, I'll be the (happier, happiest) clerk in the store.

4. After the (sad, sadly) movie was over, Henry and Tina left (quiet, quietly).

5. Father Jefferson did not speak (loud, loudly) enough for most of us in the back to hear.

6. The vet was (kind, kindly) as he stitched up the cut on the dog's leg.

7. (Sudden, suddenly) rain showers have always been common in the mountains.

8. A (good, well) plumber doesn't expect to be paid until his client is satisfied with the work.

9. Leah is quite (imaginative, imaginatively) when it comes to avoiding housework.

10. George's cabinet looks to be the (sturdiest, sturdier) of the two.

11. After her husband lost his job, Sue tried to deal with him more (patient, patiently).

12. This is the (heavier, heaviest) of all the boxes you packed; what is in it?

13. Your painting is even (more serious, most serious) than I remember it.

14. The (bigger, biggest) expense involved in owning a car is depreciation.

15. An older person may need to consult an eye doctor more (frequent, frequently) than when younger.

B. **Each of the following sentences contains one error in adjective or adverb form. Cross out the mistake and write the correct word above the line.**

1. I know your parents will be real glad to see you move back to this area.

2. My cold is worst than the one I had last year about this time.

3. Paula dances so graceful that she will probably become a professional dancer.

4. Some kinds of cheeses smell badly but taste wonderful.

C. Write in the correct form of the adjective or adverb in parentheses.

1. A computer is (easy) _____ to use than a telephone.

2. The twins are both outgoing and bright, but Brian is the (good) _____ athlete.

3. Walt's garage gave me the (low) _____ of the three estimates for the repair job.

D. Each of the following sentences has an underlined modifier phrase next to it. Write a combination that puts the modifier where it belongs in the original sentence. Write out your new sentence completely.

1. Tom watched his biology teacher setting up the practice lab.   <u>who had to take a test the next day</u>

2. Hula dancers wear skirts and leis made of fragrant flowers.   <u>made of a special kind of grass</u>

3. The farmer shuffled out to the chickens.   <u>clucking around the yard</u>

COMMON ESL STUMBLING BLOCKS: **Test A**
NOUNS, ARTICLES, PREPOSITIONS, AND VERB TENSE SEQUENCE

A. **Each of the following sentences has a mistake in noun use. Cross out the incorrect word and write the correct word above the line.**

1. One of the answer in the back of the math book is wrong.

2. Would you like to have a few snack while we watch the video?

3. Several anxious student waited outside the door to the classroom.

4. In my opinion, two of her reason for quitting her job were ridiculous.

5. Although Albert is quite intelligent, he has difficulty with simple task.

6. Each bowls of chili was made by a different member of the club.

B. **Each of the following sentences has a mistake in the use of an article (a, an, or the). Cross out the incorrect word and write the correct word above the line.**

1. Next year I hope to transfer to a University of Hawaii in Honolulu.

2. My son works as the orderly at New Hampton Regional Hospital.

3. I didn't like finding the bug in the kitchen; I hope there are no more there.

4. May I borrow your pencil for the minute?

5. I visited a Grand Canyon in Arizona last summer. What an amazing place!

6. Carmen needs to take a umbrella because the weather looks cloudy.

C. **Circle the correct choice of preposition for each sentence below.**

1. Victor's bus arrives (at, on, by) exactly 7:35 every morning.

2. The letter he was expecting came in the mail (in, on, at) Friday.

3. Chicago is (in, on, at) the state of Illinois.

4. There are several grocery stores (in, on, at) the Westerly neighborhood.

5. Don't you think that Sheena looks (as, like, as if) a model in that leather coat?

6. Irina often worries (on, about, for) her children, but she knows she has taught them well.

©2004 by Prentice Hall. PEARSON EDUCATION, INC.

D. **Each of the following sentences has a mistake in verb tense sequence. Cross out the incorrect verb and write the correct verb above the line.**

1. Natalie was washing her hair when the phone rings.

2. Were you listening while I am explaining how to get to the meeting?

3. Grace will be able to leave as soon as her flat tire was fixed.

4. Because she had hiked up the mountain for an hour, Lacey's legs are sore.

5. When I was younger, I could swimming for hours.

E. **Rewrite the following sentences to correct word order and usage.**

1. He was not knowing how to do last three math problem.

2. She was wanting to left from party when police arrive.

A. **Each of the following sentences has a mistake in noun use. Cross out the incorrect word and write the correct word above the line.**

1. Much of the informations in the catalog is helpful.

2. You may check out any of the book from the library.

3. That movies only played for a week before it left the local theater.

4. When I tried to write an essay, idea came to mind, but I couldn't organize them.

5. The distant from my home to the school is five miles.

6. Either one of the restaurant that you recommend will be suitable.

B. **Each of the following sentences has a mistake in the use of an article (a, an, or the). Cross out the incorrect word and write the correct word above the line. In some cases, you may need to insert an article.**

1. Does a roof on your house need to be repaired?

2. The winds of hurricane can do great damage, so homeowners should pay attention to warnings.

3. Her daughter works as the teacher in Phoenix, Arizona.

4. Ramon said that a movie he had just seen was a thriller about vampires.

5. We learned that the tornado is a funnel-shaped cloud containing high winds.

6. You must choose book for your report from this list.

C. **Circle the correct choice of preposition for each sentence below.**

1. I usually leave my home (during, by, at) 6:45 a.m. but not later than 7:00.

2. Michael moved from Des Moines, Iowa, (at, near, to) Louisville, Kentucky, last year.

3. The suggestion that you made is not acceptable (to, for, on) me.

4. Hector wants to ask you (for, about, on) your trip to Washington, DC.

5. She listened to her sociology lecture on tape (as, like, as if) she cleaned her room.

6. Stan intends to meet his wife and children (in, on, to) the corner of Elm and Market Streets.

D. **Each of the following sentences has a mistake in verb tense sequence or form. Cross out the incorrect verb and write the correct verb above the line, or insert the necessary helping verb.**

1. I told you that I will be late, so why were you so surprised?

2. Every year when winter comes, many people were exposed to the flu.

3. Columbus is looking for the West Indies when he discovered America.

4. Bonnie says she could do fifty push-ups any time I ask her.

5. Janie was at work for an hour before she punches in on the time clock.

E. **Rewrite the following sentences to correct word order and usage.**

1. Last night, Elaine was attended an interested lecture about economics American.

2. After last night I got home from play, I was thinking about that play for many time.

SENTENCE VARIETY: USING PHRASES WELL AND PARALLELISM   Test A

A. Label each sentence below by type - simple, compound, or complex. Write the entire word for your label.

1. I hope you will call me when you return from your trip.   _____

2. Full of hope and promise, the graduates stood as a happy group.   _____

3. We took care of their house last week, so they brought us a
    gift from their trip.   _____

4. If Beth saves enough money, she will be able to cut back her
    work hours next fall to have more time for studying.   _____

5. Breakfast is my favorite meal to eat out at a restaurant.   _____

B. Each of the following sentences contains a problem in construction, either the placement of a modifier phrase or a lack of parallelism. In the space below each sentence, write a completed revision of the sentence.

1. The vacation trip of my dreams has always been the same: a house on the beach, sunny
    weather, and the scenery is beautiful.

2. At the park, I saw a woman walking her dog from my book club.

3. Barry loves his new apartment's location, layout, and how little it costs.

4. Whoever we hire for this job must be friendly, knowledgeable, and he or she must show
    that she or he is responsible.

5. Walking along beside the creek, two woodpeckers beat out a rhythm in the forest.

6. Because he had laryngitis, Mike could not hear the man trying to call out to him.

7. Irene is an honest friend; what she says and her intended meaning are the same.

8. Last month, Rita finished her pottery class, got a new job, and she became engaged, too.

9. Dancing and laughing, the party was so much fun for Shane and Jasmine.

10. I bought a puppy from a farmer that wasn't yet housebroken.

11. Yuri is both wealthy and what a handsome guy he is.

12. I look forward to meeting my new teachers, making friends with classmates, and I want to learn more about my classes.

C. **Read the following sets of ideas. Combine each set into one sentence by transforming one idea into a modifier (word, phrase, or clause) that you can use in the sentence.**

1. Kenny was trying to tie his shoe with one hand.
   Kenny became frustrated.

2. Paula was working an extra job at the garage.
   Paula earned enough money to buy her mother a car.

3. Sam felt sick.
   Sam asked the hostess for a glass of water.

4. The dog dug a hole in the wet dirt.
   The dog was thirsty.

5. The detective was careful not to make any noise.
   The detective crept up the fire escape.

6. Malcolm wanted to prepare his car for the trip.
   Malcolm had the oil changed and the tires rotated.

7. An old barn stood near the edge of a pasture.
   The pasture was green and golden.

8. I felt proud of my husband.
   I took him out to dinner to celebrate his promotion.

©2004 by Prentice Hall, PEARSON EDUCATION, INC.

SENTENCE VARIETY: USING PHRASES WELL AND PARALLELISM   Test B

A. **Label each sentence below by type—simple, compound, or complex. Write the entire word for your label.**

1. You can learn to be a truck driver if you take a special course.   _____

2. Resources are shared in this community, and problems are discussed openly.   _____

3. Listening to the loud wind, I couldn't go to sleep last night.   _____

4. Ben introduced me to the woman who does the hiring for the hotel.   _____

5. The smoke is gone from the room, but a strong odor remains.   _____

B. **Each of the following sentences contains a problem in construction, either the placement of a modifier phrase or a lack of parallelism. In the space below each sentence, write a completed revision of the sentence.**

1. Rosemary likes to tend her garden, walking her cocker spaniel, and making beaded jewelry.

2. Sitting in the rocking chair, the scene by the lake's shore was watched by Allen.

3. Danielle bought a sweater in a cute little shop that was on sale for ten dollars.

4. Sharon is determined to lose weight, to study more, and plans on watching less TV.

5. Being unable to read at a third-grade level, Rick's teacher tutored him after school.

6. Luke is a student, a business owner, and he has two children.

7. Lying under the bed, Lisa was relieved to find her lost journal notebook.

8. Eddie and Phyllis decided to send their son to college on the day he was born.

9. Charlie watched as people left the nightclub wearing a long black overcoat.

10. Whoever gets the job must be conscientious, friendly, and show evidence that he or she is responsible.

11. I enjoy spending my free time in any one of three ways: with a book, I like to be around my kids, or with my wife.

12. Marcy can't decide whether to become a pediatric nurse, or she might like to teach children in elementary school.

C. **Read the following sets of ideas. Combine each set into one sentence by transforming one idea into a modifier (word, phrase, or clause) that you can use in the combined sentence.**

1. The prophet Muhammad was the founder of Islam.
   The prophet Muhammad was born about AD 570 in Mecca.

2. The weather was especially beautiful.
   I wanted to be outside.

3. Sabrina knows that vegetables are nutritious.
   She prefers a chili cheeseburger any time.

4. The shirts fell apart in the washing machine.
   We bought the shirts on sale.

5. We stayed away from the casinos.
   We had a good time without losing any money.

6. The cowboy was waving enthusiastically to the crowd.
   The cowboy rode out of the arena.

7. Abby brought home a kitten for her son Tyler.
   He was like a ball of orange fluff.

8. The campers sneaked some candy bars into their packs.
   They were determined not to be hungry on the trip.

A. **In each sentence, cross out errors in capitalization and write the correct capital letters above the line. Also, add the end punctuation that each sentence needs.**

1. On the fourth of july, my family plans to gather at uncle rick's house in little rock

2. The congressman will speak to the rotary club while on his campaign trip to chicago

3. Did you watch the braves game broadcast from atlanta last night on espn

4. The bombing of the murrah federal building in oklahoma city was an act of terrorism

5. What a huge diamond ring ted gave nancy

6. The seafood festival called "a taste of maine" featured lobster

7. Two of the courses I took this spring, french and accounting, were challenging but not as difficult as anatomy and physiology 165 was last year

8. My advisor asked me if I wanted to remain in professor smith's class, abnormal psychology 215

9. My niece asked me, "why did you buy tide detergent instead of a cheaper brand"

10. Do you plan to hear senator perez when she speaks in the school auditorium Monday

11. Marcy attended gallaudet university for one year before transferring to a college in the Midwest

12. George yells "hey, buddy" every time he sees his favorite cartoon character, casper the friendly ghost

13. The greek pastries sold at the bazaar on tenth street were delicious

14. You probably know that "the star spangled banner" is the name of the us national anthem, but do you know the name of canada's anthem

15. I couldn't believe aunt trudy would drink so much pepsi after the doctor told her not to

B. **Add semicolons where necessary in the following sentences.**

1. A large crowd showed up for the picnic however, a sudden rainstorm drove them inside.

2. Monica left in a hurry she never came back to the party, either.

3. Derek had only five dollars therefore he decided not to go to the movie.

4. The surgeon was stern as he explained the procedure the assistants listened intently.

5. The committee consists of Sid Byerly, a painter Marie-Jeanne Dumont, a theater director and Todd Lighthorse, a dancer.

C. Add end punctuation, capitals, and semicolons as needed.

1. I usually do not answer my phone during meals furthermore, I turn the ringer off after 10:00 p.m.

2. Her mother married her father in 1963 it was the day president kennedy was buried

3. It's amazing how do you do it

4. If you don't watch him, grandpa will eat the middle out of all the oreo cookies

5. Harold manages his finances using a software program called quicken

PUNCTUATION I: CAPITALS, SEMICOLONS, AND END MARKS   Test B

A. In each sentence, cross out errors in capitalization and write the correct capital letters above the line. Also, add the end punctuation that each sentence needs.

1. America's longest river is the missouri and the biggest lake is lake superior

2. The oldest and largest tree in the united states, located in the west, was named for general Sherman, a civil war soldier

3. Did you know that iowa is the headquarters of jiffy pop popcorn

4. My advisor recommended that I take a business course next fall, but I want to take general psychology 150

5. Little red riding hood cried to the wolf, "what big teeth you have, grandmother"

6. Franklin and jennifer invited us to celebrate mother's day with them in baltimore

7. Don called downstairs, "how long do you guys plan on rehearsing that so-called music"

8. Last october I took a french cooking class at the community college

9. Have you written a letter to senator mcbride about the excessive development in the western part of the state

10. On monday, our history professor, dr. taylor, will be talking about the industrial revolution and its effects on the economy

11. The exhibit of paintings from greek mythology was sponsored by general motors

12. "Do you belong to the automobile association of America" asked the mechanic

13. the driver of the yamaha motorcycle in front of uncle tony swerved

14. While watching his favorite TV show, "west wing," dad ate two snickers bars and a bag of doritos

15. Whenever we pass an ad for mcdonald's, the kids yell, "happy meal"

16. The best book I read last summer was poisonwood bible by barbara kingsolver who formerly had written mainly about the american west

B. Add semicolons where necessary in the following sentences.

1. Marcia's bicycle has been repaired moreover, it looks as good as new.

2. We are going to camp out tomorrow at the ticket booth we want to be first in line.

3. Many people do not use adequate amounts of sun screen while working outdoors they are surprised when they end up with a sunburn.

4. Janice wanted to make this the best party her husband had ever had therefore, she hired his favorite local band to play.

5. There weren't nearly enough hot dogs to feed the crowd we ordered five pizzas.

C. Add end punctuation, capitals, and semicolons as needed.

1. Jasmine was not present at the meeting in fact, she did not come to work all week

2. Gregory peck, who starred in the film to kill a mockingbird, died in june, 2003

3. Dad yelled, "look out don't you see that train coming"

4. Uncle brad always wears lee jeans and polo shirts he thinks he's stylish

5. Which movie did you see last night was it one you would recommend to mom

A.   Add commas and apostrophes where they are needed in the following sentences.

1. As he picked the pecans Jake tossed them into the basket on the ground and thought about the long days work ahead of him.

2. Thomasvilles parade was canceled due to the storm but it has been rescheduled for next Saturday.

3. Hermans dog an energetic Chihuahua goes everywhere with him.

4. Unless she begins to get more sleep Carla wont be able to concentrate on this semesters classes.

5. Our companys ball team needs to raise money for additional bats better gloves and new uniforms.

6. Machines that simulate natural sounds such as a mountain creek or crickets on a summer night help block out city noise.

7. Shellys sister moved from Roanoke Virginia to Lexington Kentucky to be near her widowed father.

8. My brothers advice for getting the best deal on a new car is to let the dealer know youve done your research.

9. The Millers son a recent graduate from college is starting a job near Portland.

10. If youre interested in last-minute airline ticket bargains you must be flexible in your travel plans.

11. Whenever its snowy or icy outside I listen to the radio to hear whether the schools are closed.

12. Those five artists paintings were not chosen for the main show at the gallery but they will be shown in the lobby.

13. Despite his fear of heights Donald had a really good time on the hike.

14. Anger guilt and depression are common responses to the death of a loved one.

15. Her parents fiftieth anniversary party which will be at the town hall is next week.

16. My elderly aunt whispered "Im too old for my granddaughter to be out this late."

17. Thomas please take the garbage can out to the street for tomorrows pickup.

18. Someone had stolen the two girls backpacks so they had to borrow supplies for the rest of the camping trip.

19. Whos making the arrangements for the limousine to be waiting for us at the airport?

20. The lawyers offices must be expanded or the firm will run out of space in a year.

21. Ive told you already Karen that I will not be able to come to tomorrows meeting.

22. After she graduated last December Joanie got a good job because she had been making contacts throughout her last semester.

23. "Please get out your peer review chart" the teacher said "and prepare to read your partners essay."

24. Ordinarily our biology class has a lab on Thursdays but this week we had a test.

25. My Saturday was spent washing my car cleaning out the basement and mowing the yard.

A. Add commas as necessary in the following sentences.

1. Johann Gutenberg the inventor of the printing press died in obscurity in Mainz Germany in 1468.

2. After working for years on his idea to make movable type he finally lost his business.

3. For twenty years Gutenberg experimented with ink invested money and printed scraps of material with little success.

4. Just as he was working on his greatest printing project the Bible he met with financial misfortune.

5. Finally a man named Johann Fust who had loaned Gutenberg 800 guilders for tools sued to get his payment and finished the printing of the Bible.

6. Johann Gutenberg may have died a business failure but his life's work inventing the printing press changed the history of the world.

B. Add apostrophes as necessary in the following sentences.

1. George Washington Carvers life was devoted to agriculture research; perhaps hes best known for his work with peanuts.

2. This great scientists research revealed that chemicals in the seemingly simple peanut could be rearranged into cheese, dyes, and soap.

3. The peanuts versatility inspired research on the sweet potato, from which Carver developed 118 different products.

4. The introduction of many crops that Carver recommended, such as soy and pecans, revolutionized the Souths economy.

5. Todays accomplishments and ethical questions in bioengineering would probably interest Carver.

C. Add commas and apostrophes as necessary in the following sentences.

1. I cant find the letter that states the amount of the invoice but I am sure that it was filed recently.

2. My friend Joan who is Mr. Winslows secretary is taking a vacation next week.

3. When a doctor tells you that youre going to need surgery you should seek a second opinion.

4. Did you know Mr. Hill that the sales crews next meeting has been postponed until after Fridays holiday?

5. If we do not hear from you by Thursday March 11 we will have no choice but to refer your account to a collection agency.

6. Inside the baby was crying the soup was boiling over and the toddler was splashing water in the dogs bowl.

7. Weve been reviewing the portfolios of last quarters marketing strategies.

8. Mr. Herbin the president of the company earns a salary that equals two years wages for most people.

9. After the lecture was over Dr. Ortiz told us that this weeks assignment is to collect water samples from the citys reservoir.

10. Id love to visit Hawaii but it seems that dream will have to wait another year.

11. It was not as a matter of fact my idea to accept that vendors proposal.

12. My cousin an inexperienced driver said "Its really too bad that your dads car doesnt have an automatic transmission."

13. Several workers supplies had been left at the building site so the supervisor had to go back to collect them.

14. Yes someones car is in Mikes parking place again; therefore were probably going to get a lecture about it on Monday.

PUNCTUATION III: Test A
COLONS, DASHES, QUOTATION MARKS, AND ITALICS

A.   **Some of the following sentences need a colon, and some do not. If the sentence needs a colon, insert one where it belongs. If it is correct as it is, write a C in the space next to the sentence number.**

    1. ____ Uncle Leon had only one thing on his mind making a lot of money.

    2. ____ The three committee members most qualified to be chair are Sam Townsend, Gudrun Pierce, and Norene Chambers.

    3. ____ Several courses at this college are considered difficult calculus, microbiology, and physics.

    4. ____ Some beautiful species of trees can be found in this arboretum ginkgoes, weeping cherries, and Japanese maples.

    5. ____ Some of the vitamins found in vegetables are vitamin A, thiamine, and niacin.

B.   **Each of the following sentences would be more easily understood with punctuation. Insert dashes where they could be useful to show meaning and emphasis.**

    1. Everything she said absolutely everything was negative.

    2. The final project worth 40 percent of your grade is due Monday.

    3. The winning golf team Paige, Lara, and Ginny will go to the state competition.

    4. The TV series unlike the film that inspired it was a dismal failure.

    5. She was telling the truth the complete truth for the first time in her life.

C.   **Add quotation marks in the sentences that include direct quotes. In most of these, you will also need to add commas. If a sentence does not need quotation marks, write C for correct next to the sentence number.**

    1. ____ When is the revision of this essay due? asked Jessica.

    2. ____ The waiter told us Your dinner will be served in just a few minutes.

    3. ____ Carla asked Diane if she could come in to work early.

    4. ____ I surely will be glad said the grand old woman when it's time to play bridge.

    5. ____ The librarian asked the eager twelve-year-old What is your favorite kind of book?

    6. ____ This is the end of the discussion said the boss I want you to get back to work.

7. ____ What time did he call asking for the pizza?

8. ____ Give me liberty or give me death was the famous cry of Patrick Henry.

9. ____ Come here, Mom! cried the frightened child I see a giant spider web at the foot of my bed!

10. ____ I guess you're wondering said the lawyer why I called you here today.

D. Indicate the titles in the following sentences by either inserting quotation marks or underlining to indicate italics.

1. The New York Times is one of the United States' oldest newspapers.

2. Wallace Stevens' poem The Man on the Dump can be found in the book The Palm at the End of the Mind.

3. This article titled Power Sleep is the best one in this month's issue of Time.

4. The speech commonly known as I Have a Dream was delivered in August, 1963.

5. Her favorite book is Gone With the Wind, and her favorite poem is Crossing the Bar.

A. **Some of the following sentences need a colon, and some do not. If the sentence needs a colon, insert one where it belongs. If it is correct as it is, write a C next to the sentence number.**

1. ____ Please send the following items to our office five boxes of pens, ten reams of paper, and three printer cartridges.

2. ____ Here is Lorie's biggest problem talking on the phone when she's supposed to be working.

3. ____ The recipe calls for eggs, flour, sharp cheddar cheese, and two sticks of butter.

4. ____ I sent invitations to several new neighbors the Isaacs, the Browns, and the Patels.

5. ____ Her exercise routine is always the same five miles on the treadmill and a massage.

B. **Each of the following sentences would be more easily understood with punctuation. Insert dashes where they could be useful to show meaning and emphasis.**

1. The basic needs of people food, clothing, and shelter are the same everywhere.

2. Tabitha's main goal one that occupies every thought of every day is finding a boyfriend.

3. Broccoli a nearly perfect vegetable is on almost every nutritionist's list of healthful foods.

4. Promoting my business takes me all over the state Miami, Tampa, Orlando, and Jacksonville.

5. There's no way absolutely no way that Chad will accept that low offer for his house.

C. **Add quotation marks in the sentences that include direct quotes. In most of these, you will also need to add commas. If a sentence does not need quotation marks, write C for correct next to the sentence number.**

1. ____ Let me ask the boss if I can leave early said Amanda.

2. ____ If I don't like this drama class Mollie said then I will change my major to music.

3. ____ Pablo asked his wife if he had enough time to mow the lawn before dinner.

4. ____ A mind said a popular TV ad of years ago is a terrible thing to waste.

5. ____ When are you planning to paint your living room inquired my mother.

6. ____ A poem by Odgen Nash advises When called by a panther, don't anther.

7. ____ Clean up that room! she shouted to her son Do it or you're grounded!

8. ____ Drew was thinking to himself that it was never too late to be happy.

9. ____ Have you got any idea asked Bronna where this new grill came from?

10. ____ A foolish consistency is the hobgoblin of little minds wrote Ralph Waldo Emerson.

D. Indicate the titles in the following sentences by either inserting quotation marks or underlining to indicate italics.

1. Newsweek magazine can be found in classrooms, along with reading guides.

2. A copy of Rachel's favorite Mary Oliver poem, Wild Geese, serves as a bookmark in her Bible.

3. In Cold Blood, a book by Truman Capote, is a chilling account of a real crime.

4. F. Scott Fitzgerald's book The Great Gatsby was made into a movie.

5. John F. Kennedy's book Profiles in Courage contains a chapter titled The Time and the Place.

USING THE CORRECT WORD: SPELLING, HOMONYMS, AND USAGE Test A

A. Circle the correct form and spelling of each word.

1. As the guard walked back and (forth, fourth), the tourists tried to distract him.

2. Connie's children gave (their, there) dad an ice cream maker for Father's Day.

3. (Who's, Whose) car is that in my spot?

4. Last weekend at the grocery store, Isabel (choose, chose) a new kind of cereal.

5. Do you think the candidate we have chosen for the position will (accept, except) the job we are offering her?

6. (Lose, Loose) clothes are certainly comfortable in extremely hot weather.

7. If (your, you're) going by the drug store, would you please pick up my medicine?

8. The clock that usually (sits, sets) on the mantle is being repaired now.

9. Carl first called home to check on his kids and (than, then) called his office.

10. The protesters are planning to (rise, raise) their signs when the parade passes the post office.

11. The jury is ready to turn in (its, it's) verdict, so the judge is calling everyone back.

12. The car is out of gas; that's why it won't go any (further, farther).

13. We were invited to my cousin's house for Thanksgiving, but Aunt Tillie wanted us to go there, (to, too).

14. The chef said that the kitchen will (definitly, definitely) close at 11:00.

15. If you do not have your (receipt, reciept), getting a refund will be impossible.

16. Hilda was annoyed that she and her date arrived too late for the (beginning, begining) of the movie.

17. In Tennessee Williams' plays, the (arguements, arguments) between characters are dramatic.

18. It will be (neccessary, necessary) for you to complete an application.

19. Mr. Saliers did not let anyone know that he was (disappointed, disapointed) with the outcome of the race.

20. The class is (all ready, already) for the exam.

21. The carpenters have (alot, a lot) of lumber to use in building our deck.

22. The Boy Scouts in Troop 88 have asked (every one, everyone) in the neighborhood to donate to their project.

23. Do not give too much (significant, significance) to that woman's rude comments.

24. (Everyday, Every day) we have a chance to make new mistakes.

25. The review in the newspaper gave special (compliments, complements) to the set designer.

USING THE CORRECT WORD: SPELLING, HOMONYMS, AND USAGE Test B

A. Circle the correct form and spelling of each word.

1. Kathy was upset to be (past, passed) up for the promotion because she knew she was qualified.

2. "(Accept, Except) no gift that will obligate you later," advised my father.

3. The professor called in an expert (who's, whose) traveled in Africa extensively.

4. A large, elegant vase was (setting, sitting) in the middle of the formal dining table.

5. Hiroki is (use, used) to the type of food served in this restaurant.

6. A vacation is (two, too) weeks after which you are (to, too) tired to return to work and (to, too) broke not to.

7. First we prepared the sauce ahead of time to chill; (then, than) we cut up the fruit.

8. His parents are celebrating (their, there) anniversary as (they're, there) traveling to New York.

9. The smoke from the chimney (raised, rose) to merge with dusk in the twilight sky.

10. The amount of rainfall during growing season has a big (affect, effect) on the harvest of most fruits.

11. A Frisbee loses some of (its, it's) speed as it goes a long distance.

12. The Greek salad was a nice (complement, compliment) to the main dish.

13. My parents are going on the trip (weather, whether) or not we approve of their decision.

14. Dana has other projects going on (beside, besides) painting furniture.

15. Samantha will be (quiet, quite) pleased with the birthday gift that you are giving her.

16. When someone thanks you, be sure to say, "(Your, You're) welcome."

17. You should be proud of your (acheivements, achievements).

18. Adam's (judgment, judgement) was impaired by the medicine he was taking.

19. It is not (neccesary, necessary) for you to shout to make yourself heard.

20. Everyone experiences a bit of (loneliness, lonliness) at some point in life.

21. Walter felt that is was a (priviledge, privilege) to serve other people at the soup kitchen.

22. (Unfortunately, Unfortunatly), she lost her wallet while she was on vacation.

23. Take a deep (breath, breathe) before you dive into the cold lake.

24. When my niece was engaged to be married, she bought some simple (everyday, every day) dishes.

25. After three weeks of slow recovery from the strange illness, Tammy finally was feeling (alright, all right).

ANSWER KEYS

ANSWER KEY: PART I

Prewriting and Planning – Test A

A. 1. c   2. a   3. c

B. 1. d   2. c   3. a   4. e   5. b

C. delete: *my first car was a green Camaro, aching back from bending over so much, boss really hates it if a person is late*

D. Answers will vary.

E. in order of items listed: K   D   K   K   D   K

F. Answers will vary.

G. 1. I   2. E   3. I   4. P   5. I

H. Answers will vary.

Prewriting and Planning – Test B

A. 1. F   2. T   3. T   4. F   5. F

B. Answers will vary.

C. Answers will vary.

D. 1. E   2. P   3. I

E. delete: *ran out of gas on the longest bridge, had a long layover in Atlanta, ran into high school drama teacher who had failed me*

F. in order of items listed: K   K   D   D   K

G. Answers will vary.

H. Answers will vary.

Drafting: Topic Sentence or Thesis Statement – Test A

A. 1. c   2. b   3. e   4. a   5. d

B. 1. G   2. B   3. G   4. B   5. B   6. B   7. G   8. B   9. B
    10. G   11. G   12. B

C. 1. b.   2. c

D. 1. b   2. c   3. a   4. d

E. 1. <u>The superintendent in my apartment building, Ms. Layton,</u> *treats all of us residents as she would her own children.* (italic indicates double underline)

    2. <u>My daughter's first piano lesson</u> *was a joy because of her wonderful teacher.*

Drafting: Topic Sentence or Thesis Statement – Test B

A. 1. e   2. b   3. d   4. c   5. b

B. 1. B   2. G   3. B   4. G   5. G   6. B   7. G   8. B   9. B
    10. G   11. G   12. B

C. 1. c   2. b

D. 1. d   2. c   3. a   4. b

E. 1. <u>Studying in the upstairs reading room of the library</u> *is pointless because of the constant socializing that goes on in there.* (italic indicates double underline)

    2. <u>Tina's three teenaged sons</u> *have very different personalities.*

Drafting: Unity, Development, and Coherence – Test A

A. 1. the festival had a zip line . . . 2. ~~had to buy some good . . .~~
   3. ~~Lin and Freddie had been dating . . .~~
   4. ~~family knows not to bother me when . . .~~
B. Answers will vary.
C. 1. b   2. a   3. b   4. a
D. In order down the list: 2,   4,   1,   5,   3
E. Answers will vary. Possible for 1: *However & Now*; Possible for 2: *Therefore & For example*
F. Circle words such as *she, Grandma's, means, supplies, remarkable woman, Grandma, resourceful, stretch, Great-grandmother, resourceful*
G. 1. a   2. Paragraph a: ~~The best meal she ever made . . .~~ Paragraph
   b: ~~Her dad retired after . . .~~

Drafting: Unity, Development, and Coherence – Test B

A. 1. ~~tuition was kept at the same . . .~~ 2. ~~the extra bedroom set . . .~~
   3. ~~drinking water with meals is . . .~~
   4. ~~baseball is gaining great~~
B. Answers will vary.
C. 1. b   2. a   3. b.   4. b
D. In order downward: 3,   1,   4,   2,   6,   5
E. Answers will vary. Possible for 1: *For example & Also*; Possible for 2: *First & Then*
F. Circle words such as *shy, withdrawn, timid, introverted, changes, goal, strategy, shyness, overcome*
G. 1. a 2. ~~Paragraph a: Physical education had actually been my favorite . . .~~
   Paragraph b: ~~Children need to develop hygiene habits . . .~~

Proofreading, Revising, and Editing – Test A

A. Paragraph 2:
   My best friend's mother-**in law** is the only person I know who has a realistic dummy of a man to ride with her in her car for safety purposes. Mrs. Baker calls her companion Hercules. I **have'nt** actually met Hercules, but I would like to someday because of the tales I have heard about him. For one thing, according to my **friend he** has had more than one scrape with the law. Once, when Hercules was in the back seat, apparently taking a nap, a policeman stopped Mrs. Baker to find out if she was transporting a criminal. Another time his hand was sticking out of the trunk, and Mrs. Baker was thought to be a **murderess**. Several of Mrs. Baker's **friend** have been startled when they thought a man was staring at them from the car. They thought he looked rather intent on studying their actions. Hercules looks so real that he has fooled many an **inocent** onlooker. I hope to soon see this marvel for myself!

B. Jerry is a baseball fanatic. He loves playing the game, watching the game, and talking about the game. Jerry can quote almost any player's batting average or error stats-and not ~~not~~ just the current players, but also those from throughout history. This baseball fan's ~~**ideal**~~ **idea** of a vacation is to **go** *to* **Florida**, not for enjoying the beach or Disneyworld, but to catch six or eight games during a week of spring training. Jerry even has a fantasy team with several other baseball lovers. This **is** *a* **league** of pretend teams, each of which has a regular lineup of players from real life, only put into different groupings for the fantasy team. On Jerry's wedding day, a buddy of his called up to ask if he could trade a player. Jerry actually ~~**past**~~ *passed* up a chance to get a great player and asked him to call back the next day! This is the only ~~**the**~~ time I can recall that Jerry didn't put baseball first.

C. Charlotte, a neighbor of mine who is ~~**real**~~ *really* energetic, recently returned from an educational trip with Habitat for ~~**Humanity the**~~ *Humanity. The (or other correction)* purpose of the trip was to build two new houses for families whose homes had been destroyed by flooding. Charlotte feels that she received more than she gave through this ~~**project. Because**~~ *project because* she learned so much about the work involved and how to be a part of a team. Charlotte, an inexperienced carpenter, was the only woman on the framing crew. Each worker on the team had ~~**their**~~ *his or her* own assignments. Charlotte learned how to use a level and a nail gun, tools that ~~**was**~~ *were* essential on the job. After breakfast at 6:30, the crew was hammering by ~~**7:00 a.m., workers**~~ *7:00 a.m. Workers (or other correction)* took half an hour for a lunch break and kept working until 5:30. ~~**Working at this pace for a week, nine walls and over twenty roof trusses were built by Charlotte's team.**~~ *Working at this pace, Charlotte's team built nine walls and over twenty roof trusses in one week. (or other correction)* When she got home, Charlotte called to tell me how tired but pleased she was with her work.

D. (3) Different environments result in different flavors of coffee. Not many coffee lovers know much about the plant that ends up as the drink that starts so many mornings. (2) Almost eighty countries have these characteristics and have large coffee plantations. (1) The coffee shrub requires a frost-free climate, moderate rainfall, and a lot of sunshine. ~~My favorite coffee is from Costa Rica, where there are many large coffee farms.~~ (4) The most special, and therefore expensive, coffees in the world come from the trees grown at high altitudes in the tropics, often on volcanic soil.

Proofreading, Revising, and Editing – Test B

A. Paragraph 2:
One of my favorite memories is of a weekend spent with two of my childhood **freinds** on Block Island. Block Island is located off the coast of Rhode **Island not** far from Long Island. It is a beautiful island of cliffs high above the sea. One of the activities we enjoyed was bicycling around the perimeter. The hills were tough, but the scenery was worth it. One of my friends **k n o w s** someone with a boat who took us out to Black rock where we swam and snorkeled around the base of the **r o c k**. Nearby was a wreck of a ship lying about twenty feet **down, the** water was so clear that we could float on top and see all the way down. Finally, we enjoyed exploring the quaint New England town at the harbor. The weekend on Block Island was magic: good weather, beautiful scenery, precious company, and **natures'** gifts. I will always cherish this memory.

B. At my husband's recent community college graduation ceremony, I learned something new while reading the program. It's not that I was bored; I just **tried** *to* entertain myself after his name was called and all those other students marched across the stage to receive ~~there~~ *their* diplomas. At the back of the program, there was a ~~lists~~ *list* of the meanings of the colors on the faculty members' hoods. A person who has a Master's degree wears a hood on his or her gown, and this hood has two stripes: one ~~for~~ for the university attended and the other for the subject area. For example, a white stripe signifies a degree in arts or humanities. An orange one stands for engineering. Golden yellow means science, and light blue means education. I spent several long ~~moment~~ *moments* of graduation looking at the faculty members, trying to figure out what they teach. It helped pass the time until I could congratulate my husband **with** *a* **hug**.

C. Yesterday morning at the local diner, I had an interesting encounter that taught me a lesson about my own prejudice. Since I was eating alone, I sat at the **counter, that** *counter. That (or other correction)* way, I wouldn't take up a table in the crowded little restaurant. I am a regular there, so the server soon brought me some coffee and my usual **breakfast. Two** *breakfast, two or breakfast: two* eggs over easy, bacon, hashbrowns, and wheat toast. As I **begun** *began* to eat, a neatly dressed woman sat down next to me. She ordered breakfast and started to read a book. Not recognizing her, I figured that she was a visitor and perhaps a bit **shy I** *shy, so I (or other correction)* spoke up to welcome her, telling her she'd found the best breakfast spot in the area. After a great conversation about her book, a travelogue of America's national parks, I just knew she had to be a teacher. I was so wrong. One of the biggest surprises of my life **were** *was* finding out that this petite, intelligent lady was a truck driver for a large company hauling electronics across the country. I had thought that all truck drivers were uneducated **rednecks, my** *rednecks. My (or other correction)* new friend showed me not to stereotype anyone. It was a great lesson to start my day.

D. ~~College can be a real challenge for many people.~~ (2) It may be quick and convenient to eat junk food, but the lack of nutrition will catch up with a person who habitually eats poorly. In the high stress world of college, students should take special care to stay physically fit. (1) One way to do this is to eat wisely. (3) Another concern is getting enough exercise to offset the sedentary hours spent in class and studying.
(5) Finally, a wise student will pay attention to keeping as regular a schedule as possible and getting adequate sleep. (4) A brisk walk or game of pick-up basketball can do wonders for the attention span.

ANSWER KEY: PART II

Narration – Test A

A. 1. b   2. a   3. b
B. 1. b   2. b   3. a   4. a   5. b
C. 1. a   2. b   3. b   4. a   5. b
D. 1. in order: 3, 1, 5, 2, 4   2. in order: 4,3,5,1,2
E. Answers will vary. Possibilities: 1. *then*   2. *Suddenly*   3. *First*   4. *After*
                                                    5. *finally*
F. 1. <u>A customer taught me a lesson one morning . . .</u>
   2. Answers will vary. Possibilities: *To begin with, About 10:15, Then,* and.
   3. Answers will vary.
   4. ~~I had been working at the store between school terms. . . .~~
   5. Answers will vary.

Narration – Test B

A. 1. T   2. T   3. F   4. T
B. 1. a   2. b   3. b   4. a   5. a
C. 1. a   2. a   3. b   4. a   5. a
D. 1. in order: 4, 1, 3, 2, 5   2. in order: 5, 4, 2, 3, 1.
E. Answers will vary. Possibilities: 1. *Until*   2. *suddenly*   3. *While* or *As*   4. *Meanwhile*
F. 1. <u>My twelfth birthday was originally a disappointment . . .</u>
   2. Possibilities: *preceding, When, also.*
   3. Answers will vary.
   4. ~~Meanwhile, my brother was begging for a set of tires . . .~~
   5. Answers will vary.

Description – Test A

A. 1. c   2. b   3. a
B. 1. a   2. b   3. b   4. a   5. b
C. 1. a   2. b   3. a   4. a   5. b
D. Answers will vary.
E. Answers will vary.
F. In order: 2, 4, 1, 3
G. Answers will vary. Possibilities: 1. *Beside*   2. *Under*
H. 1. <u>To my childhood sensibilities, my grandmother's small basement was a **mysterious** and **somewhat scary** place.</u>
   2. space order
   3. Answers will vary. Possibilities: *halfway down, Above it, perpendicular, still higher*
   4. ~~Moisture can get into the walls of a place and ruin the sheetrock.~~
   5. Answers will vary.

Description – Test B

A. 1. F   2. T   3. T
B. 1. a   2. b   3. b   4. a   5. b
C. 1. a   2. b   3. b   4. a   5. a
D. Answers will vary.
E. Answers will vary.
F. In order: 3, 4, 1, 2 **or** 2, 1, 4, 3
G. Answers will vary.
H. 1. <u>To my ten-year-old wandering eyes, the office where my aunt worked as the director of a nature center was a</u> **magical place**.
   2. space order
   3. Answers may include: *to the left, beside, on the left wall, across, above her desk, right wall.*
   4. ~~Aunt Sandy had lived in Costa Rica, where she had even seen an active volcano, and loved all kinds of nature.~~
   5. Answers will vary.

Illustration or Examples – Test A

A. 1. a   2. c   3. a
B. 1. a   2. b   3. b   4. a
C. 1. b   2. a   3. b   4. b
D. Answers will vary.
E. 1. c   2. d   3. d   4. b
F. Answers will vary. Possibilities: 1. *For example*   2. *Furthermore* or *Also*
G. 1. grandmother's generosity   2. money, time/talent, and love
   3. Answers will vary.   4. ~~She is also very unselfish.~~

Illustration or Examples – Test B

A. 1. F   2. T   3. T
B. 1. a   2. a   3. b   4. b
C. 1. b   2. a   3. a   4. b
D. Answers will vary.
E. 1. b   2. c   3. a   4. d
F. Answers will vary. Possibilities: 1. *For instance* or *Also*   2. *Once*
G. 1. clothes the writer doesn't wear, but which are sentimental
   2. mother's sweater, dad's jacket, gloves, little dress
   3. Answers will vary.
   4. ~~She went to college a long way away from her family in Ohio.~~

Process – Test A

A. 1. c   2. a   3. b   4. a
B. 1. b   2. a   3. b   4. a   5. b
C. 1. a   2. b   3. b   4. a   5. b
D. 1. In order: 2, 5, 1, 3, 4   2. In order: 4, 1, 2, 5, 3
E. Answers will vary. Possibilities: 1. *First*   2. *Before*   3. *Then*
F. 1. taking care of your teeth   2. healthy teeth in later years   3. commands-the subject is you understood   4. to provide a reason   5. 11   6. b

Process – Test B

A. 1. T   2. F   3. F   4. T   5. T
B. 1. a   2. b   3. b   4. a   5. a
C. 1. b   2. a   3. b   4. a   5. b
D. 1. In order: 3,5,2,1,4   2. In order: 3,2,1,5,4
E. Answers will vary. Possibilities: 1. *To begin*   2. *After*   3. *Then*
F. 1. making your own pizza at home   2. save money, have fun   3. 7
    4. Answers will vary   5. A

Definition – Test A

A. 1. c   2. b   3. d   4. a
B. 1. b   2. a   3. a   4. a
C. 1. b   2. a   3. a   4. b
D. Double underline is indicated by *italics*.   1. <u>mental condition</u> *marked by extreme sadness, inactivity, poor concentration, and hopelessness.*   2. <u>person</u> *who consistently looks for the positive aspects of a situation.*   3. <u>person</u> *who has withdrawn from allegiance to and residence in his or her native country.*   4. <u>system of governing</u> *based on the military authority of an occupying power.*
E. 1. pers   2. pers   3. tech   4. tech
F. 1. <u>Persistence is the action of going forward toward a goal despite opposition or possible danger of failure.</u>   2. 5   3. 3   4. Reba McCoy   5. 6

Definition – Test B

A. 1. F   2. F   3. T   4. T
B. 1. b   2. a   3. b   4. a
C. 1. a   2. b   3. b   4. a
D. Double underline is indicated by *italics*. 1. <u>Spanish food</u> *consisting of seasoned rice and some kind of spicy meat.*   2. <u>person</u> *who prefers his or her own company over that of others and who values independence.*   3. <u>electronic device</u> *used in medicine to overcome the effect of tremors in the muscles of the heart.*   4. <u>sea mammal</u> *that lives in warm coastal waters and has two flippers and a large oval tail.*
E. 1. c   2. a   3. d   4. b
F. 1. <u>A citizen is a person who is actively involved in community affairs on a regular, ongoing basis.</u>   2. 1   3. 7   4. volunteering at a local public school   5. 5

Classification – Test A

A. 1. c   2. b   3. a
B. 1. b   2. a   3. a   4. b
C. 1. a   2. b   3. a   4. a
D. Answers will vary. Possibilities: 1. Blizzards or heat wave   2. Games on a field or games on an outdoor court   3. Bills or appeals for contributions
E. 1. ~~things that belonged to my grandmother~~   2. ~~trip to take with close friends~~
    3. ~~teenagers~~
F. Answers will vary. Possibilities: 1. *Another*   2. *While*   3. *second*
G. 1. the reason people attended the festival   2. Another, the last group
    3. between sentences numbered 10 and 11   4. 5   5. Dad

Classification – Test B

A. 1. T   2. F   3. T   4. F

B. 1. a   2. b   3. b   4. a

C. 1. b   2. a   3. a   4. b

D. Answers will vary. Possibilities: 1. Dramas or talk shows 2. Made of fruit or made of pastry 3. Birthday or anniversary

E. 1. ~~dark~~   2. ~~dessert specialties~~   3. ~~lawnmower~~

F. Answers will vary. Possibilities: 1. *One kind*   2. *second*

G. 1. type of movie the club members enjoy   2. an example of the third kind of movie
3. 8   4. Answers will vary.   5. type, kind

Comparison and Contrast – Test A

A. 1. b   2. c   3. a   4. c

B. 1. a   2. a   3. a   4. b

C. 1. a   2. b   3. a   4. a

D. Answers will vary.

E. Answers will vary. Possibilities: 1. *Both . . .and*   2. *On the other hand*

F. 1. Size of the lots
       Neighborhood 1
       Neighborhood 2
   Types of homes
       Neighborhood 1
       Neighborhood 2
   Closeness to city
       Neighborhood 1
       Neighborhood 2
2. Car 1
       gas mileage
       horsepower
       roominess
   Car 2
       gas mileage
       horsepower
       roominess

G. 1. Myrtle Beach and Edisto Island   2. both are beautiful seaside vacation spots
3. block method, telling all the information first about Myrtle Beach and then all the information about Edisto Island
4. ~~Edisto Island, with its unusual name, is a place my uncle's family went last year.~~
5. a sentence about how Edisto Island is not crowded

Comparison and Contrast – Test B

A. 1. T   2. F   3. T   4.
B. 1. a   2. b   3. a   4. a
C. 1. a   2. b   3. a   4. b
D. Answers will vary.
E. Answers will vary. Possibilities: 1. On the other hand   2. Also or Furthermore
F. 1. Political expertise
        Candidate 1
        Candidate 2
    Community Involvement
        Candidate 1
        Candidate 2
    Views on environmental issues
        Candidate 1
        Candidate 2
    2. Teacher 1
        Knowledge of content material
        Teaching methods
        Sense of humor
    Teacher 2
        Knowledge of content material
        Teaching methods
        Sense of humor
G. 1. Tamara and Kelly   2. twins, love of family, enjoying time together
    3. Alternating method   4. ~~Tamara actually has bright blue eyes too, like my other sister and me~~.
    5. a sentence about how Kelly is quick to speak up

Cause and Effect – Test A

A. 1. F   2. T
B. 1. a   2. b   3. b   4. a   5. a
C. 1. b   2. a   3. a   4. b
D. Answers will vary. Possibilities: 1. *Consequently*   2. *Therefore*
E. Answers will vary.
F. In order: 4, 1, 3, 5, 2
G. 1. <u>*cause*</u>: weather forecast for snow   <u>*effect*</u>: family changed plans
    2. <u>*cause*</u>: more people shopping on line   <u>*effect*</u>: malls less crowded at holiday season
H. 1. <u>Going into a much larger school had several unexpected consequences.</u>
    2. consequences   3. <u>I had been the leading free throw shooter on my former team.</u>
    4. a   5. Answers will vary. Possibilities: *First, because; Another change; therefore; since*

Cause and Effect – Test B

A. 1. T   2. F
B. 1. b   2. a   3. b   4. a   5. b
C. 1. b   2. a   3. b   4. b
D. Answers will vary. Possibilities: 1. Because   2. Effect
E. Answers will vary.
F. In order: 3, 2, 1, 5, 4
G. 1. *cause*: Mr. Tucker worked with asbestos siding   effect: he developed lung problems
    2. *cause*: virus outbreak   *effect*: cruise ship company canceled three trips
H. 1. After thirty years, however, Edie has decided to change careers for several reasons.
    2. ~~When she first started driving, there were few truck stops with women's shower rooms.~~
    3. a   4. a   5. Answers will vary. Possibilities: *however; One reason; Also, because; main factor.*

Argument – Test A

A. 1. a   2. a
B. 1. T   2. F   3. T
C. 1. b   2. b   3. a   4. a
D. 1. b   2. b   3. a   4. b
E. 1. a   2. d   3. f   4. c   5. e   6. b
F. 1. K   2. K   3. D   4. K   5. D
G. Answers will vary.

Argument – Test B

A. 1. c   2. b
B. 1. F   2. T   3. T
C. 1. b   2. a   3. b   4. a
D. 1. a   2. n   3. n   4. a
E. 1. e   2. f   3. c   4. b   5. d   6. a
F. 1. K   2. D   3. K   4. D   5. D
G. Answers will vary.

ANSWER KEY: PART III

Basic Sentence Parts – Test A

A. <u>Subject is in regular print; *verb* is in *italic print*.</u>

1. dock — *needs*
2. neighbors — *bought, parked*
3. critics — *gave*
4. Most — *are offering*
5. runners — *Are*
6. Tan — *had been working*
7. design — *is*
8. cruise — *is*
9. stay — *lasted*
10. atmosphere — *is*
11. Tim, Vickie — *have moved*
12. instructor — *Does accept*
13. life — *does revolve*
14. I — *enjoy*
15. director — *gives, helps*

B. <u>As above, with **completer** in **bold**</u>

1. husband — *respected* — **decision** — (to college)
2. grandfather — *was* — **carpenter**
3. Tony, Isaac — *have bought* — **tickets** — (for the concert)
4. family — *enjoys* — **kayaking** — (on the rivers) (of this beautiful state)
5. admission (to movies) — *is* — **advantage** — (of my job) (at the concession stand)

C. <u>As above, with subjects underlined and MODIFIERS in SMALL CAPS</u>

1. AN OLD HOMELESS <u>man</u> SLOWLY *walked* along the railroad tracks.
2. THE LOCAL COMMUNITY <u>college</u> *will* SOON *begin* A NEW **semester.**
3. THE PATIENT'S FAITHFUL <u>friend</u> *paced* around the waiting room during the operation.
4. A NUTRITIOUS <u>breakfast</u> *is* THE MOST IMPORTANT **meal** (of the day).
5. THE BEAUTIFUL <u>rays</u> of the sunrise *are lighting* THE ORANGE CANYON **walls.**

Basic Sentence Parts – Test B

A. <u>Subject is in regular print; *verb is in italic print*.</u>

1. One — *noticed*
2. Harry, Nan — *closed, flew*
3. anyone — *has seen*
4. Most — *are beginning*
5. Walking — *is*
6. plans — *were submitted, accepted*
7. Both — *are working*
8. room — *was*
9. trees — *reminded*
10. students — *Did finish*

11. ability, desire   *have led*
12. some   *will be moving*
13. Grace   *has begun*
14. nurses   *were given*
15. claims   *sound*

B.   As above, with **completer in bold**
1.   Ernest   *squeezed*   **tube**
2.   photograph   *shows*   **family** (on the front porch) (of a cabin)
3.   members   *did receive*   **instructions**
     (of the jury)
4.   cousin   *can afford*   **set** (of golf clubs)
5.   sauce (in the   *tastes*   **salty**
     yellow bowl)

C.   As above, with subjects underlined and MODIFIERS in SMALL CAPS
1.   THE TRAIL <u>guide</u> *led* THE TIRED BUT HAPPY **group** up the steep hill to the lodge.
2.   THE CLOTHES <u>dryer</u> in the laundry room *emitted* A LOUD HUMMING **sound**.
3.   CRACKED AND UNEVEN **concrete** *covered* THE FORMER PATIO **area** in her backyard.
4.   THE SWEET FAMILIAR <u>smell</u> of lilacs *was* A NICE **welcome** HOME.
5.   *Is* YOUR GRANDFATHER <u>clock</u> A VALUABLE **antique**?

Joining Ideas in Sentences: Coordination and Subordination – Test A

A.   1. C <u>but</u>   2. S <u>If</u>   3. S <u>when</u>   4. C <u>so</u>   5. S <u>After</u>
B.   1. gloves, and   2. none   3. rains, we   4. days, so   5. none
     6. lunch, today   7. none
C.   Answers will vary.
D.   Answers will vary.
E.   Answers will vary.

Joining Ideas in Sentences: Coordination and Subordination – Test B

A.   1. C <u>for</u>   2. S <u>after</u>   3. S <u>Because</u>   4. C <u>and</u> 5. S if
B.   1. none   2. call, audience   3. sleepy, but   4. none   5. pay, so
     6. none   7. suit, they
C.   Answers will vary.
D.   Answers will vary.
E.   Answers will vary.

Avoiding Fragments – Test A

A.   1. F   2. S   3. F   4. F   5. F   6. S   7. F   8. S   9. F
     10. F   11. S   12. F   13. S   14. S   15. F
B.   Answers will vary.
C.   Fragments are underlined; corrections may vary.
     A counselor once told me something that surprised me at the time. <u>But which I later realized was true.</u> I had told her that I wished I had someone to take care of me. <u>She told me if I did not learn to take care of myself.</u> No one else ever would. At the time, I did not like hearing

this. <u>Feeling that it was a harsh thing to say.</u> <u>As I learned more about the challenges of life.</u> I learned that a person really does need to take care of herself. I eventually went back to visit the wise counselor who had taught me a valuable lesson. <u>To thank her for telling me the truth.</u>

Avoiding Fragments – Test B

A. 1. F   2. S   3. S   4. F   5. F   6. F   7. S   8. F   9. S
    10. F   11. F   12. S   13. S   14. F   15. F

B. Answers will vary.

C. Fragments are underlined; corrections may vary.

The Learning Resources Center on the main campus is in disarray this summer. <u>Because the walls are being painted and the carpet is being replaced.</u> Workers began by moving all the stacks of books. <u>In order to work around them.</u> They started with the first floor during the break between spring and summer terms. After classes began for the summer, the LRC had to be closed. <u>But only for three days while the first floor circulation area was painted and carpeted.</u> The biggest complaint about the work was the loss of the computer lab. <u>Which had to be shut down for two weeks due to water damage.</u> This had to be fixed. <u>Before the new carpet could be laid.</u> Now all the areas of the LRC are back in service, and the staff and students are enjoying the fresh new surroundings.

Avoiding Run-ons and Comma Splices – Test A

A. 1. RO   2. CS   3. S   4. CS   5. S   6. RO   7. S   8. CS   9. RO
    10. RO   11. CS   12. S   13. CS   14. S   15. RO   Corrections will vary.

B. Answers will vary.

C. Mistakes in the paragraph that need a correction are in bold and underlined. Corrections will vary.

Todd's aging mother has had to make some changes lately because of her physical condition. She had back surgery a few months **ago now** she has to have another operation. Todd and his wife are trying to help his mother accept the fact that she mother can't do everything she used to do. For example, she has always valued a clean **house, she** never had anyone help her with housework. Recently, Todd hired someone to do some cleaning. His mother had tried to vacuum the floors **herself, that's** one reason her back didn't heal well. She objected at first to using a **cane, she** finally gave in and started using **one, it** helps her get around. The entire family has high hopes that the next surgery will ease the **pain Todd's** mother will have to follow doctor's orders if she is going to get well.

Avoiding Run-ons and Comma Splices – Test B

A. 1. RO   2. S   3. CS   4. S   5. CS   6. RO   7. RO   8. S   9. CS
    10. RO   11. CS   12. S   13. CS   14. RO   15. S   Corrections will vary.

B. Answers will vary.

C. Mistakes in the paragraph that need a correction are in bold and underlined. Corrections will vary.

All over the United States, many people have a growing concern about the number of violent crimes by young people. Parents and teachers can watch for certain warning **signals, any** child or teenager whose life shows danger signs may need help. First, a young person needs to have a parent or caring adult in his or her life, someone to confide in and listen to. This does not necessarily have to be a **parent, it** may be another relative or mentor. The caring adult should be concerned about any child who is frequently angry or **depressed he** or she must observe whether the child is treated badly by peers. Caregivers usually know to be concerned about the company their children keep. Negative influences can cause a young person to go **astray if** he or she admires the "bad guys" too much, the misplaced admiration can lead to problems. There is a fine line between fascination with violent games, movies, and music and imagining doing violence. Failure in school is a warning **signal, the** child may look for success in another area. Access to and fascination with weapons is a warning sign that a child may be in danger of developing a tendency toward violence. Americans have a duty to pay attention to the lives of **children, lives** and futures could be saved.

Using Verb Tenses Correctly – Test A

A. 1. became   2. did   3. had   4. eaten   5. taught   6. gone
    7. meant   8. torn   9. fallen   10. began   11. sang   12. known
    13. frozen   14. taken   15. would   16. was   17. had   18. am
    19. written   20. continue

B. 1. The chemistry professor drew the diagram on the chart.
    2. The student archaeologists have found several unusual pieces of pottery.
    3. Four of the parents are taking the kids in my son's class to the zoo.

C. 1. Aunt Annie was very pleased that her son ~~come~~ came to visit her in the nursing home.
    2. My cousins thought that my new car ~~costed~~ cost more than it actually did.

Using Verb Tenses Correctly – Test B

A. 1. done   2. treated   3. saw   4. begun   5. driven   6. gone
    7. wrote   8. become   9. eaten   10. sung   11. drunk   12. given
    13. chosen   14. will   15. was   16. had   17. was looking
    18. earned   19. have wanted   20. had received

B. 1. Dave and Sandra's children prepared the entire welcome home dinner.
    2. Grandpa finally passed the driving test the third time.
    3. The work crew will paint Tommy's bedroom tomorrow.

C. 1. Ellen has already put my name on the list of people to be ~~contact~~ contacted about the party.
    2. Iris has had been homesick until she finally got off the plane and greeted husband.

Subject-Verb Agreement – Test A

A. 1. need   2. was   3. belong   4. requires   5. Have   6. makes
    7. consists   8. is   9. reads   10. watches   11. were   12. sits
    13. seems   14. is   15. plays   16. attend   17. Do

B. 1. any verb **with s**   2. any verb **with s**   3. any verb **without s**

C. <u>2nd line</u>: offers   <u>3rd line</u>: decorates . . . ~~is~~ are   <u>5th line</u>: creates   <u>6th line</u>: welcomes

Subject-Verb Agreement – Test B

A. 1. enjoy   2. considers 3. goes   4. don't   5. gives   6. are
    7. makes   8. is   9. waits   10. are   11. make   12. sets
    13. annoy   14. offers   5. help   16. starts   17. sells

B. 1. any verb **without s**   2. any verb **with s**   3. any verb **with s**

C. <u>1st line</u>: ~~consist~~ consists   <u>3rd line</u>: ~~come~~ comes   <u>4th line</u>: task of . . . windows ~~are~~ is
    <u>5th line</u>: ~~is~~ are   <u>6th line</u>: includes

©2004 by Prentice Hall, PEARSON EDUCATION, INC.

Using Pronouns Correctly: Case, Reference, and Consistency – Test A

A. 1. me   2. she   3. I   4. He and I   5. he   6. me   7. us   8. she
    9. I   10. me   11. he   12. him   13. hers   14. me   15. its
B. In some of these, revisions will vary. Answers or problems to be corrected are listed below.
    1. *he* = unclear reference   2. ~~which~~ **who**   3. *her* = unclear reference   4. *it* = unclear reference
    5. ~~you~~ **they**   6. *they* has no reference   7. ~~I~~ **me**   8. *Thurman ~~he~~ needs*   9. ~~myself~~ **me**
    10. ~~her~~ **she**

Using Pronouns Correctly: Case, Reference, and Consistency – Test B

A. 1. he   2. me   3. I   4. me   5. we   6. her   7. she   8. us
    9. they   10. her   11. I   12. you   13. his or her   14. their   15. he
B. In some of these, revisions will vary. Answers or problems to be corrected are listed below.
    1. **they** = unclear reference   2. **her** = unclear reference   3. ~~you~~ **I**   4. ~~your~~ **my**
    5. **them** has no reference   6. ~~her and her sister~~ **her sister and she**   7. **he** = unclear ref
    8. ~~them~~ **it**   9. ~~myself~~ **me**   10. ~~him~~ **he**

Pronoun—Antecedent Agreement – Test A

A. 1. them   2. his   3. their   4. his or her   5. her   6. their
    7. its   8. his   9. their   10. his or her   11. they   12. he or she
    13. they   14. its   15. their
B. 2. his   3. his or her   3. its   4. their   5. his   6. her
    7. their   8. its   9. his or her   10. its

Pronoun—Antecedent Agreement – Test B

A. 1. its   2. she   3. his   4. his   5. its   6. his   7. their   8. its
    9. he   10. he or she   11. its   12. her   13. their   14. its   15. him or her
B. 1. he or she   2. its   3. they   4. he or she   5. its   6. I   7. his or her
    8. its   9. he or she   10. his or her, his or her

Using Modifiers Correctly: Adjectives and Adverbs, Modifier Problems – Test A

A. 1. quietly   2. sincere   3. delicious   4. mature, well
    5. clearly   6. patiently   7. diligent   8. well
    9. hungrier   10. largest   11. smallest   12. heavier
    13. rainiest   14. well, better   15. really
B. 1. ~~bad~~ badly   2. ~~hardest~~ harder   3. ~~gentle~~ gently   4. ~~worse~~ worst
C. 1. more gracious   2. most popular   3. worst
D. 1. Waiting for his date to come downstairs, Ted looked around the living room nervously.
    2. Bill gave his sweetheart a necklace that he had made himself as they watched the sunset.
    3. I could see the mechanic, covered in grease and grime, working on my car.

Using Modifiers Correctly: Adjectives and Adverbs, Modifier Problems – Test B

A.   1. peaceful   2. slowly   3. happiest   4. sad, quietly
     5. loudly   6. kind   7. Sudden   8. good
     9. imaginative   10. sturdier   11. patiently   12. heaviest
    13. more serious   14. biggest   15. frequently
B.   1. ~~real~~ really   2. ~~worst~~ worse   3. ~~graceful~~ gracefully   4. ~~badly~~ bad
C.   1. easier   2. better   3. lowest
D.   1. Tom, who had to take a test the next day, watched his biology teacher setting up the practice lab.
     2. Hula dancers wear skirts made of a special kind of grass and leis made of fragrant flowers.
     3. The farmer shuffled out to the chickens clucking around the yard.

Common ESL Stumbling Blocks:
Nouns, Articles, Prepositions, and Verb Tense Sequence – Test A

A.   1. one of the answers   2. a few snacks   3. Several anxious students
     4. two of her reasons   5. with simple tasks   6. Each bowl of chili
B.   1. transfer to ~~a~~ the University   2. as ~~the~~ an orderly   3. finding ~~the~~ a bug
     4. for ~~the~~ a minute   5. visited ~~a~~ the Grand Canyon
     6. take ~~a~~ an umbrella
C.   1. at   2. on   3. in   4. in   5. like   6. about
D.   1. when the phone ~~rang~~   2. while I ~~am~~ *was* explaining   3. tire ~~was~~ *is* fixed
     4. legs ~~are~~ *were* sore   5. could ~~swimming~~ *swim* for many hours
E.   1. He did not know how to do the last three math problems.
     2. She wanted to leave the party when the police arrived.

Common ESL Stumbling Blocks:
Nouns, Articles, Prepositions, and Verb Tense Sequence – Test B

A.   1. Much of the information   2. any of the books   3. That movie
     4. ideas came to mind   5. The **distance** from my home
     6. Either one of the restaurants
B.   1. Does ~~a~~ the roof   2. winds of **a** hurricane   3. works as ~~the~~ **a** teacher
     4. that ~~a~~ the movie   5. learned that ~~the~~ **a** tornado   6. choose **a** book
C.   1. by   2. to   3. to   4. about   5. as   6. on
D.   1. that I ~~will~~ *would* be late   2. people ~~were~~ *are* exposed   3. Columbus ~~is~~ *was* looking
     4. says she ~~could~~ *can* do   5. before she ~~punches~~ *punched*
E.   1. Last night Elaine attended an interesting lecture about American economics.
     2. After I got home from the play last night, I thought about it for a long time.

Sentence Variety: Using Phrases Well and Parallelism – Test A

A. 1. complex   2. simple   3. compound   4. complex   5. simple
B. In most cases, answers will vary: Possibilities: 1. sunny weather, and beautiful scenery
   2. a woman from my book club walking her dog   3. location, layout, and low cost
   4. friendly, knowledgeable, and responsible   5. Walking along beside the creek, I heard
   6. Mike could not hear the man trying to call out to him because the man had laryngitis.
   7. what she says and what she means   8. finished her pottery class, got a new job, and
   became engaged.   9. Dancing and laughing, Shane and Jasmine had so much fun.
   10. a puppy that wasn't yet housebroken   11. both wealthy and handsome
   12. meeting my new teachers, making friends with classmates, and learning more about my
   classes.
C. Answers will vary.

Sentence Variety: Using Phrases Well and Parallelism – Test B

A. 1. complex   2. compound   3. simple   4. complex   5. compound
B. In most cases, answers will vary. Possibilities: 1. likes tending her garden, walking her
   cocker spaniel, and making beaded jewelry (or to tend, to walk, and to make)   2. Sitting in
   the rocking chair, Allen watched the scene by the lake's shore.   3. a sweater that was on
   sale for ten dollars   4. and to watch less TV   5. Unable to read at a third-grade level, Rick
   was tutored after school by his teacher.   6. a student, a business owner, and a father
   7. to find her lost journal notebook lying under the bed   8. Eddie and Phyllis decided on the
   day he was born to send their son to   9. Wearing a long black overcoat, Charlie watched
   10. conscientious, friendly, and responsible   11. with a good book, with my kids, or with
   my wife.   12. a pediatric nurse or an elementary school teacher.
C. Answers will vary.

Punctuation I: Capitals, Semicolons, and End Marks – Test A

A. All of the following, except numbers 3, 5, 9, 10, and 14, should end in periods.
   1. Fourth of July, Uncle Rick's, Little Rock   2. Rotary, Chicago   3. Braves, Atlanta, ESPN?
   4. Murrah Federal Building, Oklahoma City   5. Ted, Nancy!   6. A Taste of Maine
   7. French, Anatomy and Physiology   8. Professor Smith's, Abnormal Psychology
   9. Why, Tide, brand?" 10. Senator Perez, Monday?   11. Gallaudet University
   12. "Hey, buddy!", Casper Friendly Ghost   13. Greek, Tenth Street   14. The Star Spangled
       Banner, America's national anthem, Canada's anthem?   15, Aunt Trudy, Pepsi
B. 1. picnic; however,   2. hurry; she never   3. him; therefore,   4. procedure; the
   5. Sid Byerly, a painter; Marie-Jeanne Dumont, a theater director; and Todd Lighthorse, a
   dancer.
C. 1. I usually do not answer my phone during meals; furthermore, I turn the ringer off after
   10 p.m.   2. Her mother married her father in 1963; it was the day President Kennedy was
   buried.   3. It's amazing! How do you do it?   4. If you don't watch him, Grandpa will eat
   the middle out of all the Oreo cookies.   5. Harold intends to manage his finances using the
   software program called Quicken.

Punctuation I: Capitals, Semicolons, and End Marks – Test B

A. All of the following, except numbers 3, 5, 7, 9, and 15, should end in periods.
   1. Missouri, Lake Superior   2. United States, West, General, Civil War
   3. Iowa, Jiffy Pop popcorn?   4. General Psychology
   5. Red Riding Hood, "What . . . , Grandmother!"   6. Jennifer, Mother's Day, Baltimore
   7. "How . . . music?"   8. October, French   9. Senator McBride, state?
   10. Monday, Dr. Taylor, Industrial Revolution   11. Greek, General Motors
   12. Automobile Association of America?" asked the mechanic.
   13. The, Yamaha, Uncle Tony   14. "West Wing", Dad, Snickers, Doritos
   15. McDonald's, "Happy meal!"   16. *Poisonwood Bible*, Barbara Kingsolver, American West

B. 1. repaired; moreover, it   2. booth; we   3. outdoors; they   4 had; therefore, she
   5. crowd; we

C. 1. Jasmine was not present at the meeting; in fact, she did not come to work all week.
   2. Gregory Peck, who starred in the film <u>To Kill a Mockingbird</u>, died in June, 2003.
   3. Dad yelled, "Look out! Don't you see that train coming?"   4. Uncle Brad always wears Lee jeans and Polo shirts; he thinks he's stylish. or !   5. Which movie did you see last night? Was it one you would recommend to Mom?

Punctuation II: Commas and Apostrophes – Test A

A. 1. pecans, Jake . . . day's work   2. Thomasville's parade . . . storm, but
   3. Herman's dog, an energetic Chihuahua , goes   4. sleep, Carla won't . . . semester's classes
   5. company's ball team . . . bats, better gloves, and   6. sounds, such as . . . night, help
   7. Shelly's sister . . . Roanoke, Virginia, to Lexington, Kentucky, to be   8. brother's advice . . . you've   9. Millers' son, a recent . . . college, is   10. you're . . . bargains, you   11. Whenever it's snowy . . . outside, I   12. artists' paintings . . . gallery, but
   13. heights, Donald   14. Anger, guilt, and   15. parents' fiftieth . . . party, which will . . . hall, is   16. whispered, "I'm too   17. Thomas, please . . . tomorrow's pickup
   18. girls' backpacks, so   19. Who's making   20. lawyers' offices . . . expanded, or
   21. I've told you already, Karen, that   22. December, Joanie   23. chart," the teacher said, "and . . . partner's essay   24. Ordinarily, our . . . Thursdays, but   25. car, cleaning out the basement, and

Punctuation II: Commas and Apostrophes – Test B

A. 1. Gutenberg, the . . . press, died . . . Mainz, Germany, in   2. type, he
   3. years, Gutenberg . . . ink, invested money, and   4. project, the Bible, he
   5. Finally, a man named Fust, who . . . tools, sued   6. failure, but . . . work,
   inventing the . . . press, changed

B. 1. Carver's life / he's   2. scientist's research   3. peanut's versatility
   4. South's economy   5. Today's accomplishments

C. 1. can't . . . invoice, but   2. Joan, who . . . Winslow's secretary, is   3. you're . . . surgery, you
   4. know, Mr. Hill, that . . . crew's next . . . Friday's holiday?   5. Thursday, March 11, we   6. Inside, the . . . crying, the soup . . . over, and the toddler . . . dog's bowl   7. We've . . . quarter's   8. Mr. Herbin, the . . . company, earns . . . years' wages   9. over, Dr. Ortiz . . . week's assignment . . . city's reservoir   10. I'd / Hawaii, but   11. not, as a matter of fact, my . . . vendor's proposal   12. cousin, an . . . driver, said, "It's really . . . dad's car   13. workers' supplies . . . site, so   14. Yes, someone's car . . . Mike's parking . . . therefore, we're

Punctuation III: Colons, Dashes, Quotation Marks and Italics – Test A

A. 1. mind: making   2. Correct   3. difficult: calculus   4. arboretum: ginkgoes   5. Correct
B. 1. Everything she said—absolutely everything—was negative.
   2. The final project—worth 40 percent of your grade—is due Monday.
   3. The winning golf team—Paige, Lara, and Ginny—will go to the state competition.
   4. The TV series—unlike the film that inspired it—was a dismal failure.
   5. She was telling the truth—the complete truth—for the first time in her life.
C. 1. "When . . . due?" asked   2. told us, "Your dinner . . . minutes."   3. Correct
   4. "I surely will be glad," said . . . woman, "when it's time to play bridge."
   5. . . . old, "What is . . . book?"   6. "This is the end of the discussion," said the boss. "I
   want you all to get back to work."   7. Correct   8. "Give me . . . death!" was   9. "Come
   here, Mom!" cried the frightened child. "I see . . . bed!"   10. "I guess you're wondering, "
   said the lawyer, "why I called you here today."
D. 1. <u>New York Times</u>   2. "The Man on the Dump" / <u>The Palm at the End of the Mind</u>
   3. "Power Sleep" / <u>Time</u>   4. "I Have a Dream"   5. <u>Gone With the Wind</u> / "Crossing the Bar"

Punctuation III: Colons, Dashes, Quotation Marks and Italics – Test B

A. 1. office: five   2. problem: talking   3. Correct   4. neighbors: the Isaacs   5. same: five
B. 1. The basic needs of people—food, clothing, and shelter—are the same everywhere.
   2. Tabitha's main goal—one that occupies every thought of every day—is finding a
   boyfriend.   3. Broccoli—a nearly perfect vegetable—is on almost every nutritionist's list of
   healthy foods.   4. Promoting my business takes me all over the state—Miami, Tampa,
   Orlando, and Jacksonville.   5. There is no way—absolutely no way—that Chad will accept
   that low offer for his house.
C. 1. "Let me ask . . . early," said   2. "If I don't . . . class," Mollie said, "then . . . music."
   3. Correct   4. "A mind," said a popular TV ad of years ago, "is a . . . waste."
   5. "When . . . room?" inquired   6. . . . advises, "When . . . anther."   7. "Clean up that
   room!" she shouted to her son. "Do it or you're grounded!"   8. Correct   9. "Have you . . .
   idea," asked Bronna, "where this . . . from?"   10. "A foolish . . . minds," wrote
D. 1. <u>Newsweek</u>   2. "Wild Geese"   3. <u>In Cold Blood</u>   4. <u>The Great Gatsby</u>
   5. <u>Profiles in Courage</u> / "The Time and the Place."

Using the Correct Word: Spelling, Homonyms, and Usage – Test A

A. 1. forth   2. their   3. Whose   4. chose   5. accept   6. Loose
   7. you're   8. sits   9. then   10. raise   11. its   12. farther
   13. too   14. definitely 15. receipt   16. beginning   17. arguments   18. necessary
   19. disappointed 20. all ready   21. a lot   22. everyone
   23. significance 24. Every day   25. compliments

Using the Correct Word: Spelling, Homonyms, and Usage – Test B

A. 1. passed   2. Accept   3. who's   4. sitting   5. used
   6. two weeks, too tired, too broke   7. then
   8. their anniversary, they're traveling   9. rose   10. effect
   11. its   12. complement   13. whether   14. besides
   15. quite   16. You're   17. Achievements   18. judgment
   19. necessary   20. loneliness 21. privilege 22. Unfortunately
   23. breath   24. everyday   25. all right